Historic Bridges of Shropshire

by

Anthony Blackwall
E.R.D., C.eng., M.I.C.E., M.I.H.T.

Shropshire Libraries
and
Highways & Transport Department
Shropshire County Council

Preface

I am particularly grateful to Mrs. M. Halford, the County Archivist, for her help and guidance and that of her excellent staff in getting together the information for this little volume. I would like also to thank her predecessor, Mrs. Paget, who, some years ago, gave me a wealth of historical information, including that concerning the construction of the present Onibury Bridge.

With regard to the Borough Bridges, I am indebted to Mr. Anthony Carr and his assistant, Miss Williams, for information from the collection at present housed in Saint Mary's Hall[1].

Finally I would like to express my appreciation for all the advice and encouragement in the whole field of Industrial Archaeology given me, over the years, by Dr. Barrie Trinder. Without it I would not have felt at all qualified to set out on this task.

A. Blackwall

[1]Now housed in Local Studies Library, Castle Gates.

The Publishers would like to thank the Bridges Section of the Highways and Transport Department, Shirehall, for their help and co-operation. Special thanks to Mr. J. Fisher for his significant contributions in correlating and editing the manuscript and related material. Mr. A. Carr (Local Studies Librarian) compiled the index and we are indebted to him for doing so. Of course our thanks to Mrs. Blackwall for allowing us the privilege of publishing her late husband's work.

Blackwall, A.
    Historic Bridges of Shropshire.
    1. Bridges—England—Shropshire
    I. Title II. Shropshire Libraries
    624'.2'094245   TG58.S5

    ISBN 0-903802-31-7

Cover design and realization: Les Walton.

Published by Shropshire Libraries, London Road, Shrewsbury in association with the Highways and Transport Department, Shirehall, Shrewsbury.

Printed by Livesey Ltd., St. John's Hill, Shrewsbury.

Contents

Illustrations

Foreword

by
Dr. Barrie Trinder

Bridges more than any other structures epitomise at the same time the technological prowess and the aesthetic sensibilities of an era. Bridges are frequently used to illustrate the essence of a particular phase of civilisation. There is no better testimony to Roman engineering capability than the Pont du Gard. Nothing illustrates Victorian ingenuity better than Robert Stephenson's High Level Bridge at Newcastle or his late and lamented Britannia Bridge over the Menai Straits. In many boys' books of the 1930s Sydney Harbour Bridge appears as a potent symbol of British industrial strength and imperial power.

On a more modest scale the bridges of a region or a county reflect its history over many periods. They convey something of the fumbling efforts of our medieval forefathers to establish the most basic means of communication. The sheer numbers of late eighteenth and early nineteenth century bridges are witness more effectively than most economic history textbooks of the vast improvements which came about in the turnpike era. The similarly large numbers of Victorian bridges show that if stage coaches disappeared with the opening of railways, roads certainly did not fall into disuse. Concrete bridges of the early twentieth century are evidence of the appearance of the motor vehicle.

The bridges of Shropshire reflect much that is typical of the history of bridges in England as a whole. Those of the medieval period and those constructed in recent decades differ but little from those of any other similarly circumstanced county. The Shropshire bridges of the late eighteenth and early nineteenth centuries however are in many ways exceptional. The construction of the first Iron Bridge in 1777-1781, and the presence in the Coalbrookdale coalfield of so many of the country's leading iron-making companies have left to Shropshire a unique legacy of iron bridges, some of them of considerable size and importance, others structures of a more modest scale where iron was employed for its convenience of construction, or for its decorative qualities. The influence of Thomas Telford, Surveyor to the County of Salop from 1788 until his death in 1834 was profound. It was probably due to Telford that so many bridges were built or rebuilt in this period, and certainly, as this book demonstrates, he was responsible for the high quality of the work displayed in many of the structures of the time.

Anthony Blackwall was responsible for Shropshire's bridges from 1955 until 1979, a period during which new main road schemes and the demands of heavier vehicles on minor roads brought many changes. The county was fortunate that during this time its bridges were in the charge of an engineer who had such profound knowledge of and such sympathy with the structures of past generations. Shropshire is doubly fortunate that he spent his last years writing about the county's heritage of bridges.

Anthony Blackwall (he was normally called Tony by his family and Sam by his military and professional colleagues) grew up in a tradition of public service. He was born at Great Shelford, Cambridgeshire on 23rd June 1919, the son of the Cambridgeshire county surveyor, Colonel John Eaton Blackwall, who came of an old-established Derbyshire family. Colonel Blackwall's six children were all educated at different schools. By chance Anthony attended Wrekin College, and used to recall being driven over the Iron Bridge in a car by one of the masters. After leaving Wrekin College he was articled to his father before going to Loughborough College to study Civil Engineering in 1939.

By this time Tony Blackwall was already serving as a Territorial Army officer in the Leicestershire Yeomanry, and joined his regiment on the outbreak of war. In 1940 or 1941 he volunteered to train as a bomb disposal officer in the Royal Engineers. He served in England until 1944 when he took part in the Normandy landings. Subsequently he set up a bomb disposal school in Bayeux, before going to Nijmegen, where he was injured in an explosion. After recovering from his injuries he taught bomb disposal for Combined Operations at Westward Ho!, and spent some months at the Royal Engineers' barracks at Ripon before leaving the army with the rank of major in July 1946.

Tony Blackwall's first post-war civilian post was as a road engineer with Cambridgeshire County Council, where he remained until 1952, when he obtained a position with the West Riding council, based at Wakefield. He moved to Shropshire as Section Head: Bridges, in November 1955, becoming Executive Engineer: Bridges, when local government was reorganised in 1974. He was a member of the Institute of Civil Engineers for more than 30 years, and was much respected in his profession.

Tony Blackwall was active in many spheres of Shropshire life. He gained an interest in photography from one of his Shirehall colleagues and subsequently became a photographer of considerable ability, and a leading member of the Shropshire Photographic Society. He ran the NALGO Rifle Club for many years, and served as Church Warden at his parish church, Christ Church, Oxon, from 1968 until 1973. He taught on a part-time basis at the Shrewsbury Technical College, and maintained links with his students over long periods. He was interested in motor racing, in making models and in sketching, and found enjoyment in the activities of the Shrewsbury Travel Club and the Caradoc and Severn Valley Field Club. His interest in the history of civil engineering grew steadily. He attended courses at the Shropshire Adult College, Attingham Park, and at the Field Studies Centre at Preston Montford, and before long became a much-appreciated lecturer at both centres, and at the meetings of many Shropshire societies.

Tony Blackwall's book reveals a great deal about the man. His intimately detailed knowledge of every part of the county is abundantly evident, as is his feeling for and understanding of the work of past generations of engineers. On many occasions he describes solutions found for the problems encountered during bridge restoration projects, but modestly omits to mention his own part in achieving such solutions. Many sensitive adaptations of old structures to the demands of modern traffic which can be seen throughout the county are the result of Tony Blackwall's skill. The ways in which he retells incidents like the closure of Cantlop Bridge reveal something of his sense of humour and his appreciation of life's ironies.

Tony Blackwall's part in the restoration of the Iron Bridge was the greatest of his professional achievements in Shropshire, and it is fitting that this book should include his own account of the project. A few weeks before his retirement on 31st July 1979 he was able to show H.R.H. The Prince of Wales that the essential work necessary for the survival of the first Iron Bridge had been carried to a successful conclusion to his professional career.

By 1979 Tony Blackwall had already been in ill-health for some years, but from his retirement until his death in 1984 he worked steadily on this book, discovering in the Records Office the achievements of his predecessors in the county's service, and describing in his characteristically modest way much of his own work in the conservation and adaptation of Shropshire's older bridges. It is sad that he did not live to see the publication of his work, but Salopians are fortunate that so much of his knowledge, his understanding and his humour are encapsulated in this volume.

HISTORIC BRIDGES OF SHROPSHIRE

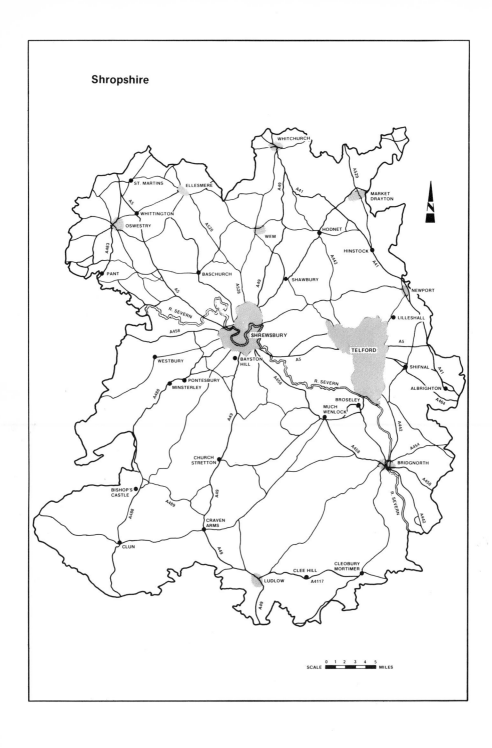

Shropshire

I

Early Days

A glance at the map of Shropshire shows the River Severn winding its way from the North West to the South East corner of the county. It is joined, in the West, before it enters the county, by the River Camlad and then by its northern tributaries, the Morda, the Perry and the Tern. The River Tern, in the North East of the county, has its own tributaries the Roden, the Strine and the Meese, referred to by Thomas Telford as the "Sleepy Meese". In the centre of the county it is joined by the Rea and Cound Brooks and farther South by the River Worfe and the Mor and the Borle Brooks. After the Severn has left Shropshire it is joined by the River Teme which comes tumbling down from the Kerry Hills, picking up the River Clun from South West Shropshire and the Onny and then the Corve, from Wenlock Edge and, finally, the River Rea, on its way.

There are, of course, many other streams draining the Shropshire countryside and this network of water courses, great and small, intersecting a corresponding network of between three and four thousand miles of County roads must give rise to a fair number of County Bridges. In addition to the natural water courses there are the various branches of the Shropshire Union Canal. Under the provisions of the L.M.S. Canals Act of 1944, bridges carrying the public highway over the, still operating, Llangollen Canal, the Montgomery Canal, the defunct Weston Lullingfields Branch, the Shrewsbury Canal and Newport Branch and the Coalport Branch all became County Bridges. In all this makes a total of about a thousand bridges. Of these, based on my acquaintanceship with them over many years as Bridge Engineer, I have selected about a quarter, which I hope will prove of sufficient interest to warrant my reader's consideration.

We will start our selection with the oldest bridges, or sites of bridges, that we can find and work our way forward from there. Where the information is available we will note the details of earlier structures on the same site as a later bridge.

What sort of bridges, surviving from the past, can we hope to find? The earliest form of bridge we might expect would be a Clapper Bridge, that is a structure consisting of large boulders, placed like stepping stones across the bed of the river, with flat stones or slabs of rock laid so as to span from one boulder to the next. Straightaway we can say we shall find none of these in Shropshire.

The Romans learnt the value of good communications, in the form of roads, and bridges to carry them, in the business of controlling and administering their Empire. Certainly they left most tangible evidence of their four hundred years occupation of this county, particularly at Uriconium, but alas, no bridge structures survive. This is disappointing, as evidence that the Romans were master bridge builders can be seen in the wonderful arch structures that have survived in Italy, France and Spain and Roman Emperors were happy to add "Pontifex Maximus" — The Greatest Bridge Builder, to their titles.

The answer is perhaps that at this far-flung outpost of the Empire the bridges were most likely military structures of timber which would have decayed very rapidly with the withdrawal of the men responsible for their maintenance. Such stone arches as were built may have survived for some years, possibly even hundreds of years. But it would have been a miracle indeed if they had survived the whole of the Dark Ages after the Romans' withdrawal, for this period lasted for about six hundred years when strife was the main occupation and certainly no maintenance can have been carried out. Trevor Rowley says, of the Dark Ages, in his *The Shropshire Landscape* — "Nowhere were they darker than in Shropshire". So there are no Roman bridges to find, but it may well be worth while looking for traces if we can establish where to look.

Another look at the map will indicate the lines followed by the Roman roads to and from Uriconium. The Watling Street from the East has few major obstacles to cross on its way to the town. However, the section of Watling Street which runs from Uriconium South-Westwards to Leintwardine must have crossed a number of water obstacles, starting with the River Severn near Wroxeter Church. Present day archaeologists have found little or no traces of what could have been WROXETER Bridge, though William Camden, in his *Britannia,* written in 1586, mentions timber remains being found during excavation in the river bed in about 1580.

A couple of miles further on its way the road had to cross the Cound Brook, about a quarter of a mile upstream of Cound Stank where we shall be looking at a pleasing bridge, built in 1779, in due course. When our road reaches a point opposite Acton Burnell it approaches the little brook there at a high level above it. Thus the Roman bridge here, RADNAL or RADNORS Bridge sprang from the top of a cliff on the North East bank and so had to have a very lofty approach embankment to match it on the opposite bank. No trace of the Roman bridge survives, but there are traces of a medieval pack-horse bridge and, of course, the impressive remains of the massive approach embankment.

Watling Street crosses several brooks in the next five miles, any of which might reward investigation of the crossing sites. After becoming the Church Stretton By-pass the old road crosses the Quinney Brook near Marshbrook and crosses open country to become the village street of Wistanstow, once part of the Coach Road to Ludlow, here at least the Plough Inn has a reward for the weary investigator. Immediately South of the village, at the Grove the River Onny must have been crossed on the site of the present bridge. There would have been no other river obstacles between here and the county boundary.

Another Roman road ran due Westwards, crossing the Rea Brook where the Shrewsbury By-pass crosses it now; the line joins the B4386, Montgomery road at Cruckton where there was a Roman Villa. The line of the old road enters the open country again after Westbury and leaves the county, into Wales along the ridge of the Long Mountain. Again the brook crossing sites which might reward the archaeologist, but no obvious traces of Roman bridges are in evidence.

So much for Roman bridges in Shropshire. But we must not leave that era without looking at a bridge which has been known locally from time immemorial as the OLD ROMAN Bridge. It comes into our sphere for consideration as a County Bridge because there is a pedestrian right of way over it. It will be found crossing the upper waters of the River Rea about a mile South West of Stottesdon, three and a half miles North of Cleobury Mortimer. It is a Scheduled Ancient Monument, registered under the somewhat prosaic title of "Bridge North of Prescott Mill," which tends to confuse it with Prescott Mill Bridge which we will look at in its place in the chronological order. To return to the Old Roman Bridge we find that, of its two stone arches, one is an "ordinary" or barrel arch of dressed stone voussoirs such as might have been built by the Romans or at any time since. The other span, however, consists of four arch ribs of similar voussoirs but with the gaps between them covered with flat stones. This achieved an economy in dressed voussoirs and made the arch lighter for the foundations to carry. The flat stones can be seen projecting at the outside of this arch, but are of course absent from the other arch.

The Old Roman Bridge over the River Rea near Stottesdon is a scheduled ancient monument.

These ribbed arches were a medieval development which virtually ceased after the Dissolution of the Monasteries (1536). There is therefore some justification in assuming that it was a monastic development easily perfected by men who could build abbeys and cathedrals. Bridge building became, in fact, an important monastic occupation, and the study of its problems the subject of so much exchange of thought between the various religious houses that a brotherhood came into being, spreading across national frontiers, throughout the Christianity of Western Europe. Monks involved in the work became Brothers of the Bridge. It would be difficult to put a date on the commencement of their activities except to say that they must have revived the art of bridge building when the final decay of most Roman built bridges, neglected since the fall of the Empire, was beginning to make itself felt.

For instance, we learn that the building of Old London Bridge, just after 1200, was planned and supervised by Brother Peter of Colechurch. Going farther afield we may consider that magnificient bridge of twenty great arches, across the River Rhone, of which now only four remain. We would find that it was built, with the help of Divine Guidance by Brother Benezet who was canonized after his death and buried in the chapel on the bridge, which is, of course, the famous Pont d'Avignon, immortalized in song. The date of its building was between 1177 and 1187.

No one seems to have been inclined to ascribe a date to the building of the Old Roman Bridge. My own assumption would be to suggest that both arches were built at the instigation of, perhaps, Wenlock Abbey which would require many such minor bridges in the maintenance of its estates. That it should have survived through the centuries, hidden away and unnoticed, is remarkable. It has been recently restored by the County Council but its use by modern agricultural machinery is a severe test.

Looking around for more ribbed arches we find one unexpectedly on the outskirts of Shrewsbury at SUNDORNE, carrying the Shrewsbury - Newport road, B5062. Before Sundorne Castle was built and later demolished, the Sundorne Brook passed under the road through a little bridge built of stone similar to that used in Shrewsbury Abbey; a diminutive ribbed arch. When the Castle was built, in Victorian times, the road was raised to form a dam, impounding the Sundorne Pool. The little stone arch was bricked up and connected, by a brick culvert, to the drain plug in the middle of the pool. A system of chains and pulleys, now defunct, served to pull out the plug and drain the pool. For the normal overflow from the pool, under the road a brick arch was built, connected to the pool via a series of weirs and called the CASCADE ARCH. At its Eastern end the dam is pierced by a large brick culvert, which fed an artificial water course running under the Shrewsbury Canal and on down to the River Severn where it helped to supply the water wheel of Uffington Mill. As the brick culvert is at a level below that of the surface of the pool, as it was constructed, it filled a small reservoir below the dam whose level was as that of the pool. The overflow from this reservoir supplied the mill. At sometime the little dam retaining the level in the reservoir collapsed, and the entire flow from the pool passed through the large culvert and the level of the pool fell

4

accordingly. This situation remains at the time of writing, with the pool much reduced and the Cascade arch dry. Uffington Mill ceased working long ago and the water course to it has been built over.

After that brief excursion into Victorian times, set off by the little old stone arch at Sundorne, our search for medieval ribbed arches takes us next to Ludlow where the road running Southwards out of the town crosses the River Teme by LUDFORD Bridge. The earliest bridge recorded here was built, probably of timber on stone piers, in about 1150 by the Castellan of Ludlow, Joce de Dinan. His bridge lasted for about three hundred years, until the present bridge was built. This consists of three ribbed stone arches springing from massive stone piers with extensive cut-waters, up and down stream, which conveniently support the commodious pedestrian refuges at road level. When the bridge was built it supported a chapel to Saint Catherine, which leads me to believe that the bridge has Monastic origins. It was about at the time that this bridge was built that the Pope ordered the Brothers of the Bridge to be disbanded.

Though none survive in the County, the practice of setting chapels on bridges was quite a popular one in the heyday of the monasteries. For one thing it was an effective form of public relations, and it also provided a base for the collection of contributions towards the cost of maintenance of the bridge from travellers who, of course, had reason to be thankful that there was a bridge for their use. Bridges were not taken for granted to the extent that they are today. We will find evidence of one other bridge chapel in the County.

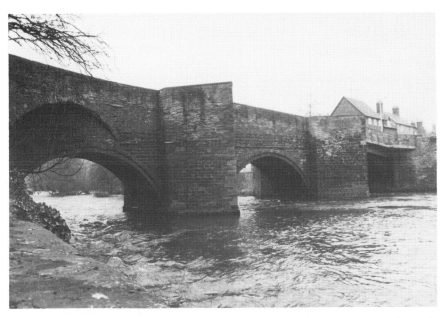

Ludford Bridge, Ludlow, showing the squint arch on the left and the more recent splay on the far side. Both additions were to accommodate traffic.

5

Ludford Bridge was built of a hard pinkish sandstone which has weathered pretty well for over five hundred years though some deterioration is becoming evident. Looking at the bridge from downstream an irregular line can be discerned running from end to end of the structure above the arches. Below the line is the old pink stone and above it a newer grey stone which is softer and already showing signs of decomposition. A plate on the parapet indicates that on the 14th May 1886 the turbulent Teme washed right over the bridge, leaving the arches intact, the piers being firmly on the bed rock, but removing most of the stonework above. The plate informs us that restoration was carried out by the Corporation of the Borough of Ludlow under its Mayor, Mr. J. E. Brooks.

At the South end of the bridge, on the downstream side is a squint-arch, splaying out from the centre of the Southern span to the bank. I think it is likely that this was added because the Mail Route to London, in coaching days, turned sharply to the left at the South end of the bridge and passed to the East of Saint Giles Church, Ludford before turning Southwards towards Ashford Bowdler. Traces of the old road can just be seen across the fields. Correspondence from the Post Office, at the time, complains of the difficulty experienced by the Mail Coaches.

A wider splay, supported on reinforced concrete beams, was built at the North end of the bridge to assist the largest vehicles to make the turn from Temeside. This was when the Trunk Road A49 passed through the town and over the bridge, before the by-pass was built. After the latter was opened to traffic this splay was partially removed to reduce its visual impact on the ancient monument.

In the ancient town of Clun, about thirteen miles to the West of Ludlow we find, scheduled as an Ancient Monument, a contemporary bridge to that at Ludford; built in about 1450 its history differs from that of Ludford Bridge in that it never possessed a chapel. This is CLUN Bridge. Smaller in scale than Ludford it has five segmental arches, two of which are ribbed and the Southernmost of which has a splay added to assist traffic approaching from Newcastle-on-Clun to make the turn onto the bridge. The cutwaters support diminutive pedestrian refuges. It is an altogether picturesque and pleasing bridge in a beautiful setting, with the impressive ruins of Clun Castle towering above. On receiving complaints from a local bus operator that the turn onto the bridge from the Newcastle road was becoming impossible, resulting in damage to both bridge and buses, I asked him to give me a demonstration. His expert hands guided the modest sized old vehicle deftly onto the bridge. "What is the problem?" I asked, "Oh, this bus is nearing the end of its time and they make them all bigger now; I can't buy one this size any more". Of such is progress and the problem of looking after ancient bridges. There appears to have been some inconsistency in the maintenance of the parapets of Clun Bridge. The parapet coping, over some of its length, consists of dressed flat stones. The remainder, however, consists of sharp-edged stones set on edge alternating with smooth, flatter stones known as "Cock and Hen". The latter form makes the pleasant custom, of sitting on the parapet contemplating the water, most uncomfortable.

Clun Bridge, Clun, built about 1450. It is very rare to find an ancient bridge of any size which has survived so completely.

It is very rare to find an ancient bridge, of any size, which has survived so completely in its original form, was the case of Clun Bridge. In 1982 the bridge was strengthened with a reinforced concrete saddle but happily there is no change in its outward appearance.

BRIDGNORTH Bridge, on the other hand, has suffered many vicissitudes and changes, adding in another way to its historic interest. It preserves an ancient crossing place of the Severn, which for a long time was the only one between Atcham and Worcester. Such was its strategic importance in the year 900 that Alfred the Great's daughter, Elfleda, "The Lady of the Mercians" instituted the building of a castle to protect the crossing which was probably a ford at that time. The first bridge, almost certainly of timber on stone piers, was built two hundred years later by Roger de Belesme. A bridge of stone arches existed in the reign of Edward II and in about 1340 Edward III granted the town the right of Pontage, that is the authority to collect tolls from users of the bridge in order to pay for repairs and maintenance. It is believed that the West or High Town end arch, a ribbed arch, may have survived from that time, making it the oldest surviving bridge structure in the county. From that time the bridge would have carried a gate-house and a chapel to Saint Osyth, suggesting monastic involvement. The historian William of Worcester recorded that the bridge consisted of eight stone arches in 1478. It was still in this form when Henry VIII ordered the dissolution of the monasteries in the late 1530s when, no doubt, the chapel was closed.

7

At this time the bridge was described as a Handsome Structure. It was however continually subject to the onslaught of the Severn floods and in 1670 two arches had to be rebuilt by Edward Paget, a freemason of Bridgnorth. These were probably towards the West end, though Paget appears to have left the ribbed arch at the West end. A description of the bridge in 1739 records seven arches, making its appearance very much as portrayed in a painting by Paul Sandby in 1778. This shows the first four arches from the West end in roughly the same form as they are now. The very massive pier between the fourth and fifth arches is shown, as now, followed by an arch and then another massive pier carrying two buildings, one on either side of the roadway, one of which could have been the remains of the chapel. Beyond that, two little arches appear which probably conducted the supply to two water wheels. Very little of the river was wasted; as a source of water supply, drainage, transport or power.

Considerable damage to various arches, calling for extensive rebuilding resulted from the floods of 1741, 1770 and the Great Flood of 1795, which played such havoc with most of the bridges along the Severn. In 1800 designs and estimates were invited for the repair and general tidying-up of Bridgnorth Bridge. A drawing authorized by Thomas Telford and dated 1802 shows a proposal to widen the bridge throughout and to remove the large pier on which the two buildings were situated, to replace the little mill arches with a single arch and to replace the fifth arch from the West end. The other large pier would remain and carry a new gate house. This would make the bridge consist of six arches of equal span with a large pier between the fourth and fifth arches from

Bridgnorth Bridge, Bridgnorth, preserves an ancient crossing place of the Severn, which for a long time was the only one betwen Atcham and Worcester. (Photo. A. Blackwall).

the West end; roughly as the bridge is today, in fact, except for recent widening. This suggests that Telford's proposals were largely carried out.

Up to this time the many phases of repair and replacement, using the stone of the repairer's choice, must have resulted in the bridge presenting a somewhat motley appearance. A contemporary report by William Hardwicke states that it had "incurred the wag's appelation of 'linsey' from the various coloured materials with which it had repaired".

A record of work carried out by Thomas Simpson in 1813 also suggests the execution of Telford's proposals. In 1823 John Smallman of Quatford widened the roadway over the third and fourth arches from the West end, carrying it upon the cast-iron arch ribs. Parapet railings of the same material were also provided for these two arches. Though this provided an essential element of widening to a narrow section of the bridge it was hardly sympathetic to the character and appearance of the old masonry bridge. At the same time Smallman did, however, tidy up the stone work including the rebuilding of at least one stone arch, believed to be the second from the West end and introduced the monumental niches in the piers. After this Hardwicke was the first to agree that it was now "The handsomest structure on the Severn".

The bridge continued in this form until 1960 when the volume of vehicular and pedestrian traffic demanded an overall widening. The incongruous and now inadequate ironwork could be removed from the two narrow arches and the bridge widened along its whole length, within cash limits. This would mean using modern materials but, if possible, keeping up the standard of the "Handsomest Structure". Much careful thought was given to this by the County bridge staff in consulation with the Royal Fine Arts Commission. It was decided to carry the widening on pre-stressed concrete beams, alongside the arches and supported on the cutwater projections of the piers. Owing to the taper of the latter the outermost beams needed to be some seventy feet long, and as they would be in full view they were clad in reconstructed stone matching that of the masonry. All the beams were cast at the Tarmac Vinculum Works in Wolverhampton. The beams were tested by the application of a load at mid-span and the deflection noted. In the case of the longest beams the deflection was four inches and it was quite surprising, to those who had not witnessed it before, to see the massive concrete beam quickly regain its original shape.

It was agreed that a simple and unexceptional form of parapet railings should be used, rather than attempting to match up with with the original stone parapets which are still in evidence round the pedestrian refuges.

Some accommodation bridges, built by estate owners, away from the public highway, for the convenience of tenants and estate workers, have survived from early times. NEENTON DAIRY FARM Bridge over the upper waters of the River Rea, about half a mile South of the village of Neenton, is one of these. Built at an early though unknown date, this bridge came to light when a right of bridleway over it came under the jurisdiction of the County Council. Possibly built for the Wenlock Abbey Estate, but more likely later, the bridge was in a disastrous state when taken over. The immediate intention was to reduce the remains to the bare abutments and span them with some form of steel and timber deck. However a closer inspection suggested that the small flat stones, of which the bridge was constructed, should be conveniently available on waste stone dumps and a complete restoration was possible within the cost allowed. The result of the restoration is quite an interesting little example of an early rubble arch in fair condition. A look under the arch reveals the holes in the abutments into which were fitted the beams, carrying the temporary timber "centres" upon which the arch was originally formed.

On the Southern border of the County, crossing the River Teme to the town of Tenbury Wells (in the county of Hereford and Worcester) is TENBURY Bridge, of six stone arches. The three nearer the Shropshire bank are ribbed and claimed by some to be fourteenth century work. The remaining three arches are of later, perhaps eighteenth century, construction. The ribbed arches were only twelve feet wide and in 1812, according to a report, some years later, to Worcestershire Quarter Sessions "Mr. Telford, an engineer" (sic) had reported on the state of the bridge and prepared a widening scheme costing £1,200. A contract was drawn up with John Simpson of Shrewsbury, dated 12th May 1814, for the widening using cast-iron arch ribs. Under Telford's supervision the work was completed in 1815. The improved width was then under sixteen feet, possibly to match the width of the remaining arches. In 1868 the County Surveyor of Worcestershire prepared a scheme to widen the bridge along its whole length, on the downstream side, using cast-iron ribs. As the bridge was widened in 1908, using reinforced concrete, after the removal of all the earlier cast-iron widening work, it is impossible to tell if the 1868 proposals were carried out. It seems likely that they were as there are records of ironwork being supplied by the Coalbrookdale Works. The cast-iron parapet railings, incorporated into the concrete widening in 1908, could well have been cast by Coalbrookdale for the 1868 widening.

A modest two-span stone arch bridge carries the Bridgnorth - Ludlow B4364 road over the Mor Brook at HARPSWOOD. When built in the seventeenth century the bridge was only seven feet wide. However, when Telford's assistant, Thomas Stanton, reported on its condition in 1810, prior to carrying out extensive repairs, the bridge had already been widened, on the upstream side, to twelve feet. Complaints about this width of twelve feet were still being received in 1826. The County Surveyor in 1839, Edward Haycock, described it as "an ancient bridge recently widened on the downstream side". This final widening brought it to its present width of eighteen feet.

The old lane which runs South-Westwards from Rushbury village, eventually reaching the Ludlow - Much Wenlock road at Diddlebury, appears to have been a pack-horse way. Where it crosses the Eaton Brook it does so over the five feet wide RUSHBURY PACK HORSE Bridge, just South of the village. All that is left of the bridge is the arch ring, of about ten feet span, and the abutments, of seventeenth century construction. It would be a worthwhile restoration project to rebuild the parapets, spandrels and wing walls of this Scheduled Ancient Monument.

South of Clunton, off the Clun - Craven Arms B4368 road, there was CLUNTON Footbridge, over the River Clun. This intriguing old structure

Llanyblodwel Bridge was built at the expense of the town of Oswestry in 1710. The centre span is a four-centred arch of forty feet giving it a peaked Gothic appearance.

caught the eye of E. Jervoise, on his research travels in the 1920s. At that time it consisted of stone piers supporting a timber deck and hand-rails. Though the timbers had fairly recently been replaced it suggested to him a really old bridge. He mentions it in his *Ancient Bridges of Wales and Western England* with an illustration. There is now apparently no trace of the old footbridge. A concrete bridge for farm vehicles occupies what is believed to be its original position.

We now move into an era when dates tended to be recorded and can be quoted with some confidence. Attention to architectural detail was becoming an important aspect and bridges were being built with a claim to being an art-form in themselves. The first bridge to come to our notice, in this category, is over the River Tanat, in the village of Llanyblodwel, a mile from the Welsh Border. LLANYBLODWEL Bridge is a fine structure of dressed red sandstone, consisting of three arches. The centre span is of forty feet and is a four-centred arch which gives it a peaked, Gothic appearance. This, combined with the shallow depth of spandrel and parapet gives an impression of airy elegance. The two side arches of nineteen feet each are segmental. As the width of the bridge is but ten feet the cutwaters are continued up to parapet level to provide pedestrian refuges. The lack of width results inevitably in frequent damage to the parapets from modern traffic. There is no record of the architect responsible. As the bridge lies in what was the Hundred of Oswestry, it was built at the expense of that town in 1710 as can be seen from the date stone. Llanyblodwel Bridge

11

received major repairs in 1886 and was taken over by the County in 1899. In 1820 Thomas Telford received a fee and travelling expenses for visiting the bridge and preparing a scheme for improving the course of the River Tanat, in the vicinity, on behalf of the Oswestry Corporation. This did not involve the bridge structure.

The first bridge to carry the important crossing of the River Severn at ATCHAM was built under the jurisdiction of the Abbot of Lilleshall Abbey soon after 1200. He was authorized to collect tolls for its use. This bridge was replaced in about 1550 by a public spirited local landowner, Sir Rowland Hill of Attingham who, about that time, was Lord Mayor of London. His bridge is said to have consisted of eighteen arches. It might be asked why such a wide reach of the river should been chosen for an important crossing. The answer is that a broad and therefore shallow point on the river would have been the ideal site for a ford and so the earliest crossing would have been established in that form. By the 1760s Sir Rowland's bridge was becoming overdue for replacement.

Atcham was one of only eight bridges which comprised the total responsibility of the County at that time. The Clerk of the Peace, who constituted the (Part-time) County Administration, therefore reported to the Magistrates Court, who were the decision making body, that a new bridge should be contemplated. Designs were invited and, in 1768, John Gwynn, an architect born in Shrewsbury but whose practice was in London with an office in Saint Martins, submitted the successful proposal. This was for the present bridge which has survived in the form in which it was built. This is a fine structure of Grinshill stone, seven semi-circular arches and two smaller openings through the wing walls. The parapets rise to a peak over the centre arch, capped by a prominent pediment-shaped feature enclosing the tablet with the date and the architect's name. The tops of the cutwaters are embellished and the whole is a good example of bridge design as an art-form, a stage further than that reached by Llanyblodwel, sixty years earlier. Tenders were invited for the construction of the bridge and on 20th July 1768 the County entered into a contract with Richard Buddle to build the bridge for £5,000. He operated from a London office in the Strand. Buddle was paid £1,200 on account and work was started.

After four years no appreciable progress had been achieved, no doubt due to problems posed by the very permiable gravelly bed in which Buddle was attempting to establish the foundations of his piers on timber grillages and driven piles.

At this point Sir Rowland's old bridge suffered severe flood damage causing some alarm in the County Executive. The part-time Treasurer had, hitherto, only to find about £500 a year for the administration of the County, which involved mainly the maintenance of the eight County Bridges and the returning of vagrants to their place of settlement. Here, on the other hand, was expenditure on a comparatively vast and apparently uncontrollable scale for which funds had to be raised by levying a rate on landowners. At this point Buddle asked to be relieved of his contract and Gwynn took over, subject to an increase in the overall cost. One source suggests the final cost to have been over £8,000. However Gwynn successfully completed the work in a further four years, in 1776.

The bridge continued to carry the traffic of the Holyhead Road until 1929 when the adjoining concrete bridge, which will be dealt with in the appropriate chapter, was opened and the old bridge happily pensioned off and preserved. The foundations which gave so much trouble in the construction receive regular attention from engineering divers. General maintenance is greatly assisted by the use of sophisticated modern access equipment.

No sooner had Atcham Bridge been completed than trouble became evident, only half a mile Eastwards along the same road, at the point where it crosses the River Tern. Here TERN Bridge, which had also been built by Sir Rowland Hill in Tudor times, was in trouble. The County Treasurer was faced with further massive fund raising. This time the successful proposal came from an architect whose practice was in Shropshire, William Hayward. He decided to cover the full width of the Tern with one span of ninety feet, the largest span in the County, to be used by traffic, at that time and still the longest masonry arch. Arches of these proportions were giving bridge builders almost insoluble problems of weight distribution. The great weight of filling material in the spandrels compared with far less weight over the crown of the arch could result in spectacular collapse with the keystone being forced violently upwards.

At Pontypridd, near Cardiff, in 1755, William Edwards eventually succeeded in constructing a masonry arch over the River Taff, with a span of one hundred and forty feet, but only after nearly ten years of frustrated endeavour and collapse. The fact that the Taff is tidal at this point made a clear span essential to avoid pier foundation scour problems. Edwards' final and successful solution (the bridge stands to this day) was to lighten the spandrels by constructing tunnels through them, the ends of which were left open. Hayward must have noted Edwards' experiences very seriously. This is shown by the fact that the only surviving drawing of Tern Bridge, a longitudinal section along the centre of the roadway, dated 28th October 1777, shows three circular stone culverts through each spandrel, similar to those used by William Edwards at Pontypridd. As no elevation drawing of the bridge survives it is not known if Hayward originally intended to construct tunnels and to leave their ends open. If they were constructed they must have been enclosed. There is now no means of confirming the existence of these spandrel vaults short of excavation.

Having approved the design, the Justices authorized the Clerk of the Peace to draw up a contract, which was signed on 13th January 1778, with William Hayward, to carry out the construction, using best Grinshill or similar stone. As the bridge was built at the expense of the County it is surprising that such a high degree of ornamentation was permitted. However reference to the tablet on the parapet tells us that it was "decorated at the expense of Robt. Hill Esq.". Attingham Hall was at that time still in the possession of the Hill family who were doubtless glad of an opportunity of enhancing the landscaping of the park by having the bridge as a major point of interest. It was completed in 1780. In 1932 it was widened by a reinforced concrete extension of the arch but re-using the external masonry. There is no record of spandrel vaults being found during this operation. It is assumed that "Best Grinshill Stone" was used in the construction of Tern Bridge, though for recent repair work it has been found that Bath stone is the best match, impact damage to the North parapet being all too frequent. It is perhaps interesting to note that on 16th April 1793 an account was received from John Carline and John Tilley for "Getting stones out of the river and repairing the bridge, including providing 24 new balusters at eight shillings each". There is something all too familiar about this. History does keep on repeating itself.

Maintenance and repair of these beautiful old bridges, in my time, was carried out by a master mason, the late Mr. Clifford Bennett and sometimes Mr. Noel Griffiths, both County employees. Without their skill and experience little could have been done. There were always problems for us to solve and not always to do with stone. One morning Mr. Bennett and his apprentice son went out to start work and, on arrival at the bridge, were horrified to find a large pool of blood in the road. They found, however no other evidence of an accident. Eventually, in the adjoining field, they did find an unfortunate swan which had flown into overhead wires and almost severed its neck. It was nevertheless still alive and the loss of blood had stopped. Very much a caring man, Mr. Bennett offered the injured bird water which it drank avidly. For the next week or two he and his son shared their meals with their patient whose strength improved daily until it was able to fly. Though it showed quite a marked reluctance to leave its benefactors it did finally continue on its interrupted journey. Happily work on the bridge continued with equal success.

At the same time as designing and building Tern Bridge, Hayward was also involved in similar work for a smaller bridge carrying the old Roman road, which is the South West leg of the Watling Street, over the Cound Brook at Cound Stank. The second turning to the right off the A458 road, after leaving Cross Houses for Cressage, leads to it. The present minor status of this section of the Watling Street gives the impression that the bridge was built for a road of greater importance. COUND STANK Bridge is a two-span structure of ashlar masonry consisting of eighteen feet span segmental arches. All is well finished with projecting voussoirs, featured keystones and false keystones at the quarter spans in the facing ring. The cutwater on the central pier is embellished. The parapets are finished with string course, plinth course and flat coping. Altogether it is a most pleasing bridge with a date stone inscribed 1779.

Hayward went on to design the original timber bridge at Coalport, which we will look at with the Iron Bridge. He then completed his final work, the three-arch ashlar masonry bridge over the River Tern at WALCOT MILL. It is a well finished structure of three fifteen feet segmental arches with two slender piers, the cutwaters of which are continued up as half columns, topped with finials and there are cartouches on the spandrels. There is a tablet that reads "The last Bridge built by that ingenious Architect William Hayward, 1782". The bridge, still in its original form, is so narrow that its parapets frequently suffer impact damage. Its Northern approach passes over a blue brick and lattice girder bridge of twenty feet span, fabricated at the Horsehay Works and erected by Robert Everall and Sons in about 1890.

An unexpected find on the Southern outskirts of Market Drayton is WALKMILL Bridge, carrying the minor road from Market Drayton to Sutton over the River Tern. It came under the jurisdiction of the Shropshire County Council comparatively recently when a boundary re-alignment transferred it from Staffordshire. Taken over with the bridge was a cast-iron notice saying "This bridge, which is a county bridge, is insufficient to carry weights beyond the ordinary traffic of the district and owners, drivers or persons in charge of locomotive traction engines or other ponderous carriages of unusual weight are hereby warned not to pass, and are desired to take notice that they will be held liable for any damage that may be caused by such engines or carriages passing over or attempting to pass over the same." It is to be hoped that the speed of the "Ponderous carriages" was such that the drivers had time to note all the information set out for their attention. The bridge is of well finished block in course red sandstone, the span of the single arch being twenty-two feet. The keystone on the downstream side is inscribed "I.S. Fecit 1783". It was confirmed and recorded at a meeting of the Justices, in 1840, that the date refers to the construction of the bridge and that it had not, up to that time, been widened. There is no evidence of it having been widened since and the present width is only about twelve feet. The height of the parapets has been increased by about a foot at some time by the insertion of an additional course of point-dressed stone, the ridged coping stones being put back on top.

On the boundary between the County of Shropshire and the Welsh County of Clwyd, about a mile West of Chirk is PONT FAEN over the River Ceiriog. This is a well proportioned, segmental, masonry arch of forty-one feet span, giving a further impression of lightness due to the fact that it is narrow, only eight feet between parapets. John Ogilby (1600-1676) the map publisher, refers to the bridge and in 1762 a report on its condition was called for by the Justices which resulted in repair work being carried out. Nine years later tie-bars through the spandrels were recommended, to hold the bridge together. More than seventy years later tie-bars were again recommended. Perhaps this time the advice was heeded as iron tie-bars have at some time been fitted.

A mile and a half East of Chirk the Ceiriog is again spanned by a smaller and even narrower bridge at PONT Y BLEW, believed to be contemporary with Pont Faen. Due to a boundary change at some time Pont y Blew now stands wholly in Wales, but in 1808 it was under Telford's jurisdiction and his approval and signature are at the foot of an instruction to carry out repair work.

At PEN Y BONT where the Llanyblodwel - Bala road, B4396, crosses the River Cynlaith into Wales, there is a stone arch of twenty-six feet span. There used to be a plaque on one of the parapets which stated "This Bridge was erected with stone at ye equal charge of the County of Denbigh and ye Hundred of Oswestry in ye County of Salop A.D. 1718". Reference is made to it in a report of 1836, when repairs were carried out. There is also reference in correspondence to a plan for a new bridge drawn by Mr. Thomas Parker in 1821. Presumably it was not executed as the present structure is recorded in the 1901 Bridge Register as being in existence in 1803, the year of an important Bridges Act.

II

The Iron Bridge and Coalport Bridge

So far we have been looking at bridges constructed exclusively of stone, with some timber involved in the earliest days. However while William Hayward was wrestling with the problem of making the ninety feet stone arch of Tern Bridge stable by introducing spandrel vaults Thomas Farnolls Pritchard, a well known and successful local architect, was considering a new approach to building a one hundred feet arch over the River Severn at Coalbrookdale.

The Iron Bridge, cast at Coalbrookdale and erected in 1779. Surely Shropshire's most famous bridge.

16

Thirteen men of business in the industrial area of Coalbrookdale, including a land-owning parson and Pritchard, were convinced that a bridge, connecting the two sides of the gorge, through which the Severn flowed, would be of great value to the development of the area. The existing facility was an overworked ferry. Their prime consideration was urgency, the need to build the bridge quickly and economically and so obtain an early return for their not inconsiderable investment, which eventually totalled over three thousand pounds between them. The driving force appears to have been provided by the ironmaster, Abraham Darby III, then only twenty-four years of age and one of the thirteen. It was however Pritchard who believed that cast-iron was the material they should choose in order to achieve their purpose. Large supplies of it could be made available and local expertize in its use was probably not equalled anywhere else in the world at the time. John Wilkinson, the ironmaster of Broseley, was also one of the group.

Pritchard's first idea was to replace the massive timber frames, called "centres", upon which a masonry arch had to be supported during construction and which had to be disposed of on completion, by permanent centres in the form of cast-iron ribs. As no iron bridge of any size had been built before this, the uncertainties emanating from the use of an untried material would be mitigated by the joint use of stone as a well established one and the finished article would combine the strength of both. An example of this form of construction can be seen in Magdalene Bridge in Cambridge, built more than forty years after the Iron Bridge. By the autumn of 1775, a year later, Pritchard was considering an all-iron bridge based on the lines of the remarkably sophisticated timber frame arches which were popular at that time, but of which none have survived. He may have been impressed by the large span bridges of this type built in Switzerland, particularly that over the River Rhine at Schaffhausen. This developed its strength by combining flattened ribs of large radius, efficient in providing resistance to earth pressures behind the abutments, with more steeply cambered ribs of smaller radius which are efficient in carrying the weight of traffic. The surviving drawing of this design, which appears in the *Architectural Journal* of July - August 1958, illustrating a paper by Robert Maguire and Peter Matthews, suggests this influence. The design in this form however did not get beyond Pritchard's drawing board.

In February 1776 Thomas Addenbrooke, secretary to the bridge promoters, arranged for a petition to be presented to Parliament asking for an Act authorising the construction of a toll bridge. The reason for this procedure still stands: any organization, not being a statutory highway authority, must obtain an Act of Parliament to authorise the building of a bridge over a navigable river. Royal Assent was given a month later.

In May of the same year an advertisement appeared in the Press asking for quotations for the building of a single arch, over the Severn between Madeley and Broseley "of stone, brick or timber". The impression given is of a temporary loss of nerve on the part of the sponsors. Pritchard was by now a sick man. Possibly the reason for this decision was a belated attempt to ensure that all the options had been investigated. It should be appreciated that a business proposition was being promoted, not the provision of a monument for posterity. Apparently the replies were disappointing as Pritchard's all-iron design was back in favour by the following month and so it remained until October 1777 when Pritchard died.

Young Abraham Darby found himself managing the technical as well as the financial problems of the project. He decided to abandon Pritchard's design, possibly because of its meagre headroom of only a little over twenty-five feet above normal water level. Darby then proposed an almost semicircular arch, providing about fifty feet of headroom to enable vessels to pass without unstepping their masts. It remains a mystery as to who draughted the detail design for the bridge. Certainly no design drawings appear to have survived. It has been suggested that the design was developed in chalk, full size, on the pattern floor at the Coalbrookdale Works by Thomas Gregory, the foreman pattern maker, under Darby's direction. There is also a suggestion that Daniel Onions, perhaps a relative of John Onions, the Broseley ironmaster, was involved on Darby's behalf. Credit for the design is usually shared between Thomas Farnolls Pritchard and Abraham Darby III whose expertize and courage resulted in the successful construction of the bridge. Darby was not only gambling with his reputation as an ironmaster and the chance of being involved in a disaster but also with his onerous personal financial investment in the project.

Much has been written, comparatively recently, on the building of the bridge: notably in *The Iron Bridge* by Neil Cossons and Barrie Trinder which must be the definitive work on the bridge and is strongly recommended to the reader. We will therefore touch briefly on this aspect and through the succeeding years of the bridge's life, until the 1970s when, as a County Bridge it became the object of a massive, joint restoration project.

Work on the construction of the bridge started with the foundations and masonry in 1778. The ironwork, when cast, was erected in three months, without incident, in 1779; the total weight being three hundred and thirty-three tons. The order and method of placing the iron ribs and other members, over the river without interrupting navigation, continues to be the subject of speculation among engineers. A paper was presented, on the subject, by John Smith of the North East London Polytechnic, under the auspices of the Institution of Structural Engineers in 1979. The bridge was opened to the toll-paying public on 1st January 1781. So much interest was shown by the public, in the whole building operation, that the track across the fields, from the Holyhead Road at Attingham Lodge, to Leighton was made into a turnpike road to carry sightseers from Shrewsbury to the bridge site. It is now the B4380 road.

The finished bridge consisted of an arch of cast-iron ribs and deck spanning one hundred feet between the two monumental stone abutments, each pierced by a small brick archway. Not long after the opening the Southern abutment was in trouble due to its own great weight. The iron arch happily survived this *contre-temps* but in 1800 the South abutment was replaced by one much smaller, farther up the valley side and connected to the main arch by two approach spans of timber. Twenty years later these were replaced by two arches of cast-iron ribs on slender stone piers, as they are today.

In about 1900 Sir Benjamin Baker, the engineer largely responsible for the Firth of Forth Railway bridge, examined the Iron Bridge and found it to be in reasonable condition but recommended the reduction of the dead weight of road material it was carrying. Correspondence from that time relates the trouble the Toll collector experienced as there was no established toll for motor vehicles.

By 1923 there was concern for the safety of the bridge and a detailed survey was made by Consulting Engineers Mott, Hay and Anderson who recommended some remedial work and a loading restriction for vehicles. In 1934 it was restricted to pedestrian traffic only, which at one halfpenny a head, meant virtually no income to pay for essential maintenance. Finally, in 1950, the Trustees of the bridge, without sufficient funds to cover cleaning and painting the structure, handed it over to the County Council to be maintained as a County Bridge. A programme of cleaning, painting and repairing was put in hand immediately.

In 1950 there was very little, if any, information available for the engineer taking the bridge over, about its history or the causes of its troubles. The assessment of these became a long drawn out operation. The first examination of the ironwork located twenty-six cracks. These were carefully recorded and any new cracks recorded with their dates of occurrence. This part of the operation indicated that the majority of cracks were caused by pressures resulting from the gradual collapse of the masonry in the North abutment. The minute annual reduction in the distance between the abutments was also measured over a period of years. The outcome of this, together with the fact that no major member was fractured, was that the structure appeared to be secure for the time being. A decision was reached, at the Shire Hall, that complete restoration must now be the ultimate objective. That this should become the massive joint operation that it did, involving the Government Department, the Ironbridge Gorge Museum Trust and the Telford New Town Corporation as well as the Shropshire County Council was far beyond the most optimistic dreams of those concerned at the outset.

Details of the Restoration Project are set out, for those who are interested, in the Appendix at the end of this book.

Coalport Bridge

In 1777, the year following that during which the Trustees of the Iron Bridge promoted their Bill in Parliament, another group of trustees promoted a similar Bill to construct a toll bridge over the Severn, just two miles below the Iron Bridge. This second bridge is located, in the terminology of that time, as "Spanning from Preen's Eddy, in the Parish of Broseley, to the Sheep Wash, in the Parish of Madeley". It was known in its early days as Preen's Eddy Bridge.

This structure was designed by William Hayward and constructed of timber by Robert Palmer, in time to be opened to the public on 25th April 1780, several months before the opening of the Iron Bridge. Palmer was the owner of a timber business in Madeley Wood. The bridge, as built at that time, consisted of two

Coalport Bridge is downstream from the Iron Bridge and was built as a three-rib structure in 1799 by John Onions and John Guest. When the centre rib fractured some twenty years later another two ribs were added and the abutments improved. The date on the midspan panel refers to this work.

The midspan panel of Coalport Bridge.

timber frame arches of about sixty feet span each, springing from masonry abutments with a midstream masonry pier. All the superstructure and deck were also of timber. The design and construction of timber frame arches had reached a high degree of sophistication by about 1750. A painting by Canaletto, in the Dulwich College Collection, shows Old Walton Bridge over the River Thames with the timber-work displayed to great advantage.

Coalport Bridge survived as an all-timber structure until 1795 when a very cold winter produced exceptional flooding along the length of the Severn, damaging many bridges and, in the case of this bridge, by virtually demolishing the midstream pier. Inspired by the example of the Iron Bridge, which survived the flood intact, the Preen's Eddy Trustees determined to modify their bridge into a single span structure supported on three cast-iron ribs. This was carried out, in 1799, by John Onions of Broseley and John Guest. Observations in the Minutes of meetings of the Trustees suggest that the deck and the rest of the superstructure remained of timber. The Bridge remained in this form for nearly twenty years, when the centre iron rib fractured. This resulted in a reappraisal of the whole situation. In spite of the failure of the iron rib the Trustees decided to make the whole structure of iron and increase the number of ribs from three to five. This time John Onions carried out the work, which also involved the construction of extensive brick piers on top of the existing stone ones; the year was 1818. The date with the initials "J.O." on the midspan panel of the iron parapet refers to this operation.

The bridge became known as Coalport Bridge after the village which had grown up around it. Due largely to the Hay Canal Incline which delivered cargoes, from the whole of what is now Telford, down to the River Severn, it became a port of some magnitude. Highway tolls were collected on the bridge until 1922 when the County Council took it over and freed it from tolls. Maintenance was delegated to the District Council, until the 1930s when the County took over that responsibility commencing with a major overhaul. One of the troubles the bridge was suffering from was the serious instability of the cast-iron parapets caused by the fact that wrought iron packing strips had been fitted in the joints between the cast-iron panels. Wrought iron rusts very much more readily than cast-iron and the strips swelled with the rust causing pressure, which burst the parapet away from the edge of the deck. The whole parapet, on both sides had to be secured with tubular scaffolding which provided the additional security of restricting the roadway to one-way traffic. Individual vehicles were restricted to two tons weight at ten miles an hour, only one vehicle on the bridge at a time. All these restrictions are ignored in varying degrees. Efforts to prevent over-loading by heavy vehicles by stopping them, in *flagrante delicto,* and confirming the offence, by checking their weight, seem always to result in a sudden absence of such vehicles using the bridge. This is a pity because the ultimate destruction of the old bridge will inevitably result from repeated overloading and excessive speed. For some years after the extinguishing of the tolls, in 1922, the Toll-keeper Mr. Green, and for many years after his death, his indomitable daughter, protected and preserved the old bridge by persuading drivers of large and heavy vehicles to "Back-up" and not go across.

Due to its continuation as a working vehicular bridge the preservation of Coalport Bridge presents a very different problem from that of the Iron Bridge. It was scheduled as an Ancient Monument in the 1970s and a scheme was prepared by the County to restore the parapets and strengthen the deck with concealed reinforced concrete. This was carried out in 1981 by the County Council, on a cost shared basis with Telford Development Corporation. As part of the scheme a sophisticated device involving electronics and fibre optics was installed at the bridge to warn drivers of vehicles which it finds to be overweight, to stop and not cross the bridge. It was developed as a prototype by the Transport and Road Research Laboratory. This operation has certainly delayed the disintegration of the bridge for, it is hoped, many years. However as the criterion for the strength of the bridge lies in the cast-iron arch ribs, which cannot be strengthened without major disfiguration, the weight and speed restrictions remain. The visitor to the bridge will note that each of the five ribs has an individual, helical twist. As the spandrel frames, fitted in 1818, are all purpose-made to accommodate the shape of the ribs, it remains a mystery how the twist, in each rib, came about. There are many theories but I feel that the most acceptable one is that, when they were cast, all the ribs warped in cooling.

The visitor will also note that the name of the public house adjoining the bridge is called *The Woodbridge Hotel,* remembering the days when the bridge was made wholly or partly of timber and was no doubt known as The Wood Bridge to distinguish it from its iron neighbour up-stream.

III

The Thomas Telford Era
1787 to 1834

The North and West

The ever-increasing pressure of road traffic towards the end of the Eighteenth Century highlighted the need for a more sophisticated organization for the construction and maintenance of public highway bridges in the County. The financial difficulties attendant upon the building of the Atcham and Tern Bridges must have provided further evidence of the problem. At this time important highways were maintained by the Turnpike Trusts and minor roads by the Parish Council Surveyors, but these authorities were not responsible for any bridges. In the 1780s only eight bridges were administered by the Clerk of the Peace as County Bridges. The responsibility for providing and maintaining all the other bridges rested with the community living in the locality of the bridge concerned. The County had powers to enforce action by charging responsible communities with failing to maintain or renew a bridge. The fine would be set at a figure which would comfortably cover the cost of the work required. This usually resulted in the work being carried out rather than the fine paid. The County could also contribute a grant towards the cost of the work and, on satisfactory completion, could admit the structure as a County Bridge. A bridge in a town would be the responsibility of the Corporation concerned.

It was, undoubtedly therefore, to the great good fortune of the County that at this time the local MP and landowner, William Pulteney, sponsored the introduction of a young architect and builder who had been practising in London in the company of such giants as Robert and James Adam. This was Thomas Telford, born in Scotland and trained as a stonemason, now in his early thirties and already fairly experienced and confident. This confidence was borne out by events at his introduction to building matters in Shrewsbury. Pulteney suggested he should inspect the work in progress at the base of the tower of Old Saint Chad's Church. Telford reported that the collapse of the tower was imminent and would not be prevented by the current work. In his opinion all labour should be withdrawn from the building; in fact he would rather discuss it outside. This was duly dismissed by the church authorities as a ploy to impress them. However, as the church clock started to strike the hour of eight, the following morning and the verger was inserting the key into the door to let the workmen in, the tower did collapse with a mighty roar. No introduction could have been more effective. He was appointed County Surveyor of Bridges, a part-time appointment as were those of the Clerk of the Peace and the Treasurer.

At that time the Clerk of the Peace was negotiating on behalf of the Justices for the reconstruction of PLATT MILL Bridge, over the River Perry at Ruyton-of-the-Eleven-Towns and accepted the proposal of a local builder, Edward Cureton, for the design and construction of a new bridge. He proposed to build a bridge of two sixteen feet span sandstone arches, with extensive wing-walls at the Ruyton end, pierced by a small flood arch. The paramount importance of founding the abutments and midstream pier soundly upon timber grillages, supported on timber piles, in order to deal with a treacherous subsoil, was stressed in correspondence. The surviving drawing of this bridge is a very rudimentary sketch, suggesting that the stonemason responsible for the building work had a lot of freedom to exercise his skill and judgement. The result is a straightforward bridge of two segmental arches without any frills, but certainly soundly built. Evidently Telford was satisfied with it as he authorized payment to Edward Cureton, the contractor, on completion in 1791. The bridge is still sound though rather narrow for modern traffic. Its foundations, particularly those of the central pier, are occasionally threatened by the dredging of the river. Should the timber grillage be exposed to the air it would almost certainly disintegrate.

The circular Toll House at the East end of the bridge was erected for the Burlton and Llanymynech Turnpike in 1841. The end of a river bridge was always a good place to locate a turnpike gate as it would be difficult for traffic to circumvent it.

The part-time aspect of Telford's appointment as Surveyor of Bridges is illustrated by the fact that, in 1790, he was paid three guineas by the County for producing the design drawings for MONTFORD Bridge. At the same time he was engaged to inspect the construction work for £200. This important bridge carries the Holyhead Road, A5, over the River Severn, four miles North West of Shrewsbury. Some thirty years later Telford was to be responsible for the reconstruction of the whole of the Holyhead Road for the improvement of the Irish Mail service, as agent for a Parliamentary Commission, on behalf of the Postmaster General and not connected with his Shropshire appointment.

The Justices, having approved Telford's Montford Bridge Plans, Specification and Estimate, which was for £5,800, entered into a contract with John Lowden and John Brawn of Oakengates for getting well-axed red sandstone blocks from Lord Bradford's quarry on Nesscliffe Hill. The rate of delivery had to be forty tons per week at nine shillings and sixpence per ton. The waggons carrying it had to have wheel tyres not less than six inches broad. A further contract was awarded to Lowden and Brawn to build and maintain a temporary bridge of timber to carry the highway traffic while the new bridge was being built. As the latter was sited about fifty yards upstream of the old bridge it is not clear why a temporary structure was required. No doubt all concerned

Montford Bridge, designed by Thomas Telford and built by John Carline and John Tilley in 1792.

would have been happier without it, as it was a constant source of trouble with the barge and trow operators who found it an obstruction and frequently damaged it. Telford had a standard design of temporary bridge supported on timber pile trestles, which he frequently used. It was designed to provide an adequate passage for navigation, as did the temporary timber arch centres.

The contract for the construction of Montford Bridge was awarded to John Carline and John Tilley, supervised on site by Matthew Davidson of Langholm, an acquaintance of Telford's younger days. He was a strict and conscientious overseer and work proceeded smoothly, without overspending and the target date for completion, Lady Day 1792, was duly achieved. The result is a fine bridge of three eliptical arches of dressed red sandstone, one of fifty-eight feet and the other two of fifty feet span each. An item in the accounts which catches the eye is for "Taking off prisoners irons and putting on again — 5 pence each" paid to the local blacksmith, Francis Cotton. No doubt the employment of prison labour helped to keep costs down.

The Turnpike Toll House at the end of the bridge was built a year later, in 1793. It was therefore not part of Telford's improvement of the Holyhead Road.

In 1963 when it was over one hundred and seventy years old, continuous severe frost forced the sides of the bridge outwards, necessitating the restriction of its use to single line traffic. The bridge, as it was built, was only twenty feet wide, providing inadequate accommodation for modern vehicles and none for pedestrians. It was therefore decided, in conjunction with the Government

Departments concerned and the approval of the Royal Fine Arts Commission, to incorporate the widening of the bridge and the provision of two footways, with the repairs. In order to avoid a long closure of the road, prefabrication was employed where possible. About two hundred deck units of reinforced concrete, each weighing three tons, were cast during the spring and summer, at the County Highway depot while traffic continued to use the bridge. At the end of the summer, as the North Wales holiday traffic slackened off, the bridge was closed for only eleven days while the new deck, roadway and footways were completed.

Some people had expressed doubts as to the ability of the old foundations, particularly those of the midstream piers, to carry the additional material as well as the greatly increased weight and speed of the traffic. The foundations were probably based on a timber grillage of two layers of planks. Care was therefore taken to remove as much filling material as the stability of the arches would allow, to compensate for the additional weight of concrete. The fact that the bridge carries the heaviest vehicles at high speed without distress speaks volumes for the soundness of the original masonry and for the care taken in its maintenance over the years.

Highway Bridges, built in the County during Telford's incumbency as Surveyor, appear to fall into two categories; first are those which were designed by him or by Thomas Stanton on his behalf and under his direction, to replace existing County Bridges or to replace other structures, which then became County Bridges. The second category consists of bridges, built at the time by local communities, to their own design but to Telford's satisfaction and which then became County Bridges. There are therefore many bridges included in this chapter which may well have been designed elsewhere. Where there is no evidence of Telford's involvement it is, of course, not claimed. He did persuade the Justices to increase the number of County Bridges from eight to one hundred and fifteen. It is now over one thousand.

Before leaving Montford it is worthwhile investigating two small bridges over the River Perry, not far above its confluence with the Severn, a mile or so downstream from Montford. The first is a twenty feet span, red sandstone arch, MYTTON Bridge, built in about 1800. The intriguing feature, to me, about this bridge is the way the layout of the wing walls with their cylindrical finials, follows very closely the layout of Montford. It would be satisfying to find the connection. Thomas Stanton, who joined Telford in 1805 and operated from the canal office at Ellesmere, inspected Mytton Bridge in 1823 and commented unfavourably on its width and vulnerability to traffic damage, but it appears to have survived in its original condition nevertheless.

Further on up the Perry we find FITZ Bridge, near the village and mill of that name. This is an old sandstone bridge, very narrow and consisting of one span of a little under twenty feet. The whole of the arch has, at some time in the not too distant past, been replaced by one of Stafford Blue bricks, effectively providing the strength but destroying the character of the bridge.

Another mile up the Perry brings us to the village of Yeaton. Here YEATON Bridge is a single brick arch of similar proportions to the last two bridges. It is quite a pleasing structure though it has rather new brick parapets. It has no documented history but would belong to this period.

A further two miles upstream takes us to MILFORD Bridge which provides the somewhat larger waterway of two segmental arches of sixteen feet span each. A plan drawn and signed by Thomas Stanton, for T. Telford and dated 1831, is a typical example of the fine, conscientious work Stanton invariably did on behalf of his chief. He was a great believer in the provision of an ample waterway as an insurance against flood and scour damage to the foundations. He also believed in a good width between parapets to avoid damage there. He must have had many struggles with an indignant County Treasurer. The condition of this bridge after more than a hundred and fifty years is testimonial enough to his principles. The contract for building Milford Bridge, which replaced a "Pack and Prime" (horse and pedestrian) bridge of three stone arches in 1831, was let to Nathaniel Edwards.

About two miles to the South West of Montford Bridge a small tributary of the Severn passes under the Shrewsbury - Welshpool road A458, Northwards through the village of Ford and into the river. The bridge by which the one-time turnpike crossed the brook is WELSHMANSFORD Bridge. The trustees of the turnpike met in December 1791 and decided that the brook should be bridged, eliminating the ford, and the road widened. The following January a plan was prepared for them by Andrew Thomas. This was of a stone arch of six feet span to be built for £38 17s 5d. Work was started in the spring and soon completed. There is no record of Telford being consulted or the County approached for a

Chirk Bridge, another Telford design constructed by John Simpson of Shrewsbury in the late 1790s.

grant or to take the bridge over. It has since been much widened, the original structure being partially immured under the centre of the road.

While work was proceeding with the construction of Montford Bridge, Telford was preparing to replace another bridge carrying the Holyhead Road; this was CHIRK Bridge, over the River Ceiriog, South of the town, at what was then the Welsh boundary so that the bridge was jointly the responsibility of Shropshire and Denbighshire. Agreement was reached between the two counties and a lofty masonry arch of fifty feet span was to be built. Each abutment was to be supported on "A platform consisting of two thicknesses of oak planks, laid one crossing the other; one layer six inches thick and the other layer three inches thick, heading joints properly broke and pinned together with one and a quarter inch wooden pins". This was to be set three feet three inches below the bed level of the river. A contract was entered into with John Simpson for carrying out the construction for which he was paid £1,093. By 1831 Thomas Stanton had to arrange remedial work where the unruly Ceiriog was undercutting the Shropshire abutment. In 1844, under the direction of Edward Haycock, a system of breakwaters was set up to divert the flow away from the abutments. With some variations to suit the changes in the river's behaviour, this protection has been maintained to the present time and is still effective. In the 1920s the bridge was widened in reinforced concrete, faced with the original masonry.

About three miles West of Oswestry, at Rhyd y Croesau, the Oswestry - Llansilin road, B4580, is carried over the River Cynlaith, which forms the Welsh boundary at this point, by RHYD-Y-CROESAU Bridge, a modest rubble masonry semicircular arch of fifteen feet span. A plan, which may have originated in Denbighshire, dated 1818, shows the bridge as it is now. The plan has been approved and signed by "T. Stanton for T. Telford".

There is a brick span of uncertain date, but evident antiquity, about three quarters of a mile to the West of St. Martins, on the road to Weston Rhyn, B5070, known as ESGOB MILL Bridge. With a span of ten feet it is well finished and quite an elegant little example of the use of brick. No records appear to exist of its construction which may well have been on behalf of the original owners of the mill. Records do show, however, that it was built before the Bridge Repairs Act of 1803.

The B5069 road, running North East from St. Martins towards Overton crosses the Shell Brook, which is the county boundary, over BARTON'S Bridge. Telford is usually credited with being responsible for the design and construction of this dressed sandstone arch of fourteen feet span, supported on high abutments. The latter enable the road to be carried at a height of about twenty feet above the brook, no doubt eliminating what must have previously been dangerously steep approaches. The date stone says 1819 though unfortunately no records have survived of the design or construction.

Starting from Oswestry in a generally Southerly direction it is possible to find a number of bridges built while Telford was County Surveyor. About a mile down the Welshpool road, A483, is MORDA Bridge, a twenty feet span dressed sandstone arch fairly typical, in detail, of the bridges designed by Thomas Stanton for Telford, though no records appear to survive supporting this impression. The date stone says 1807. Through the Northern wing walls is a nine feet brick arch, possibly added at a later date as a flood arch but for many years enclosed and used as a store. Morda Bridge became a traffic hazard and was widened by extending both arches in reinforced concrete, faced with artificial stone in 1978.

The Trefonen road, South West out of Oswestry, crosses the River Morda at LLWYNYMAEN Bridge, about a mile and a half from the town. Here Thomas Stanton reported in 1827 that the existing bridge, which had been widened in 1788, was in poor shape and should be replaced. The Trustees of the Oswestry — Llanfyllin Turnpike accepted the report and agreed to reconstruct the bridge, the County having agreed to contribute £100 towards the total cost of £600. In November 1828 Stanton reported the new bridge to have been substantially built and this fifteen feet span rubble masonry arch bridge was duly taken over as a County Bridge.

Between Morda and Llwynymaen Bridges the river is spanned by PENYLLAN LANE Bridge, but no records survive of the construction of the twelve feet span rubble masonry arch bridge. It was probably built by the local landowner and has been maintained in very good condition.

There are two small bridges over the Morda, downstream of Morda Bridge; one is to the West of Ball Chapel and known as BALL Bridge and the other is PAINT MILL Bridge, half a mile further down the river. Both are beautifully finished, dressed stone bridges, of twelve feet span with single course parapets and ornamental arch facings.

The next bridge relevant to this chapter is MORTON Bridge, over the Morda, carrying the Knockin - Llynclys, B4396 road. While there is no record of its construction, Thomas Stanton inspected it in October 1827 and reported that some of the coping stones from the upstream parapet had been removed and thrown down. "From the account of the Road Surveyor, it appears that this mischief has been wilfully done. They have not been able to trace the offenders". A notice offering £5 reward for information leading to the apprehension of the miscreants was posted. The first time I inspected this bridge, in the 1950s, I had to write a very similar report. It would appear that behavioural patterns of certain elements of our community do not change over the years. It is a well proportioned and detailed red sandstone arch bridge and almost certainly the design originated in Telford's office in about 1800.

South of the Oswestry - Queens Head road and immediately west of Queens Head stands Aston Hall, surrounded by its park, now the site of Oswestry Golf Course. The Western tip of the lake, in the park, is spanned by the three arch ASTON HALL Bridge, of brick and measuring fifty feet over the three arches. Built by the owner of the Hall it was eventually accepted as a County Bridge as it carries a minor public road. The bridge was notable for a warning notice, slightly less verbose than that at Walkmill Bridge, Market Drayton, in Chapter 1, but remarkable in that it was put up only about fifty years ago. It says: "This bridge is insufficient to carry weights beyond the ordinary traffic of the district. Owners of engines and other ponderous carriages are therefore warned against attempting the passage of this bridge. William H. Butler, County Surveyor and Bridgemaster".

By the end of 1808 Telford was planning a new bridge to carry the Llynclys - Llansantffraid road, A495, over the River Tanat, half a mile South of Llanyblodwel. Known as RHYD MEREDYTH, the existing bridge was no longer safe. Proposals were considered for a major diversion of the road in order to obviate the regular flooding of the bridge approaches. The diversion was finally abandoned and Telford decided to use a single arch of eighty feet span and twenty feet rise, lifting the roadway to nearly thirty feet above the level of the river. The approaches were also raised accordingly. As the new bridge would now be built on the site of the old one, a temporary bridge would be required and this was sited thirty yards downstream. Similar to that used at Montford, it consisted of two thirty feet and two twenty feet spans; each span being supported by king post trusses with their apexes at the top of the parapet railings and rising from brackets on the supporting piles just above water level. Completion date for the temporary bridge was February, 1809.

Foundations for the permanent abutments were specified as four feet below bed level and supported on eight inch diameter short timber piles, driven in pairs at two feet intervals. The abutments themselves were to be fifteen feet thick at the base and twelve feet at the top. A few years earlier Telford would probably have insisted on the reduction of weight at the quarter points of the arch, by means of spandrel vaults. (See Ashford Bridge). This time he decided against it and it would be most interesting to know his reasons for the decision.

On Telford's recommendation the contract was awarded to John Simpson of Shrewsbury, for completion by midsummer 1810. Dressed stone for the arch voussoirs, quoins and suchlike came from the Quarry at Plas Kynaston and from Sweeney Mountain, while the rubble came from Trevlock. As at Montford work proceeded well, according to plan. From the Accounts it will be noted that workmen were paid from two shillings to two and sixpence (10p to 12½p) per day, according to skill.

[The North and East]

The Telford scene must now move Eastwards to GREAT BOLAS Bridge, over the River Meese. It lies South of the village and within sight of it. The County Justices entered into a contract with Richard Madeley and his son, in 1795 to construct a new bridge for £221 "To a plan prepared by Mr. Telford". The plan shows a substantial structure in ashlar masonry with careful attention to string courses, pilasters, projecting voussoirs and keystones and pleasantly curved wing walls. The drawing, though clear and adequate, is in some contrast with the very high standard of draughtsmanship achieved in the later drawings which were signed "T. Stanton for T. Telford". At this stage Telford had ten years on his own before Stanton was to join him. Of course the surviving drawing of Great Bolas Bridge may be an unknown draughtsman's copy. The twenty feet span arch is almost semicircular and was covered, over the whole of the extrados, with four inches of puddled clay. This was to prevent water soaking through from the roadway and penetrating the joints in the arch. This exclusion of water is an absolutely essential element in all structures, and Telford's attention to it, ahead of other bridge builders, is a good example of his farsightedness. The condition of the arch of this bridge today is evidence of its effectiveness. The datestone says "Built by Richard Madeley 1795".

Moving upstream for a mile and half brings us to SHEEP Bridge, a very poor old bridge held together with tie bars. It consists of a central stone arch of seventeen feet with two little four feet flood arches built of brick. The whole has been extensively repaired and renewed in red brick from time to time and presents rather a woebegone appearance. No records can be found of its history or when it became a County Bridge.

A mile and a half further upstream is Caynton Mill, a brick building built almost on top of CAYNTON MILL Bridge, by which the Meese flows under the road. Now a private house, the mill was once supplied via a stone culvert, which survives, under the road a few yards from the bridge. The mill is interesting in that its motive power was provided by a turbine. A hundred yards to the West the road is carried over an alternative course of the river on a steel troughing bridge perhaps eighty years old. A little farther still, up the road there is an ancient stone arch, now dry but which used once to enable another mill to be supplied by the river.

Still travelling upstream, after a couple of miles STANDFORD Bridge is reached. A good view of this three span red sandstone bridge can be had from the modern pre-stressed concrete structure which now carries the Newport - Whitchurch road, A41, permitting the old bridge to survive in retirement. Reference is made to a contract, dated 1803, with John Simpson of Shrewsbury for its construction, no doubt "To a plan drawn up by Mr. Telford" of which no trace remains.

The is no doubt at all about Telford's connection with the next bridge, two and a half miles up the Meese. This is PULESTON Bridge which carries a minor road running Northwards from the A41 at Chetwynd Park. A plan signed by Thomas Telford and dated 1811 shows a dressed sandstone bridge, consisting of a centre span of fifteen feet with spans of twelve feet either side. The midstream piers were founded on short timber piles. When Telford drew up the specification for the construction of this bridge he headed it "Puleston Bridge over the Sleepy Meese". The site of the bridge remains a most peaceful spot to this day. It was built by John Simpson, the date stone indicating that it was completed in 1812. In 1835, shortly after Telford's death, an underpinning operation became necessary to stabilize the piers on their short piles. This was successfully carried out by Joseph Hant. The glacial silt, from the last Ice Age, which forms much of the North Shropshire plain, often gives treacherous support to foundations, particularly if the bed of firm clay, just below the surface, is penetrated. This perhaps enhances the use of comparatively shallow foundations on flat timber grillages which were so popular at this time.

Finally, on the Meese, a mile and a quarter above Puleston, is FORTON Bridge, carrying the Newport - Eccleshall, A519, road. This bridge, though similar to Puleston but with two nine feet span arches, would not have been Telford's work, as it was in Staffordshire when it was built and became a

Stoke River or Stoke-upon-Tern Bridge, built in 1789. The ornamental facing ring of the main arch shows a finely finished stepped extrados. (Photo. A. Blackwall).

Shropshire County Bridge by means of a boundary change.

Having traced the work of Telford and his contemporaries up the Meese it would be logical to follow up its parent river, the Tern, from its confluence with the Meese. The first Telford era bridge to be encountered is three quarters of a mile North of the village of Ollerton and is over a minor tributary of the Tern. OLLERTON Bridge is a ten feet span brick arch, faced with red sandstone which also forms all the rest of the structure. The masonry finish is good and in fair condition. The facing voussoirs are complemented by a prominent keystone which, on the downstream side is engraved with the initials "J.M." and the date 1829.

The village of Stoke-upon-Tern lies a mile further up the river and STOKE RIVER or STOKE-UPON-TERN Bridge is to the West of it. This is a substantial and well finished bridge in red sandstone ashlar masonry. The main span measures thirty feet with two smaller side arches of four feet each. The ornamental facing ring of the main arch is finely finished with a stepped extrados. The barrel of all three arches is of brick. The general finish of the masonry is excellent except for the topmost course of stonework on the parapets which is of rough point dressed stone and about eighteen inches deep. Though no documentation exists regarding the construction of the bridge, it is known that it was built by local subcription and the date stone indicates that this was in 1789. In 1826 Thomas Stanton reported on the good condition of the bridge but commented that the height of the parapets was quite inadequate for safety and recommended raising them. He repeated this recommendation two years later and in 1837 the urgent need to raise the parapets was repeated by Edward Haycock, by then County Surveyor. The Clerk of the Peace firmly denied County responsibility on each occasion. The comparatively inferior top eighteen inches of the parapets suggests that at sometime the responsibility was finally accepted.

The Tern flows under the re-aligned Newport - Whitchurch road, A41, through a flexible, corrugated steel "Armco" culvert which virtually floats on the apparently bottomless bed of peat and glacial silt. A mile and a half upstream from there the Northern drive to Buntingsdale Hall is carried over the river on a privately built stone arch BUNTINGSDALE HALL Bridge. It is in generally poor shape, with a decided sag in the arch. All that is known of its construction and history is summed up on the date stone: "WT 1794 WM".

A mile upstream again lies Walk Mill Bridge, with which we have dealt in Chapter 1. Half a mile beyond that brings BERRISFORD Bridge into view, carrying the minor road from Market Drayton to Chipnall and Cheswardine, described in a 1800 report as a Turnpike Road from Drayton to Eccleshall, via Chipnall. It is a single twenty-two feet span brick arch bridge , faced with stone and with dressed stone parapets and abutments. The date stone suggests that it was built in 1791. The fact that it was built by local subscription, to replace a ford and timber footbridge, is recorded. Underpinning of the West abutment was carried out in 1830 after a report by Thomas Stanton.

Half a mile further up the Tern is SHIFFORDS Bridge, a twenty-two feet span stone arch bridge with short, curved wing walls. In 1960 it was widened to three or four times its original width by extending the arch in reinforced concrete, in anticipation of the Market Drayton A53 by-pass which was built nearly twenty years later.

The final bridge over the Tern in Shropshire is BEARSTONE Bridge, two miles South of Woore, on the Loggerheads - Woore road, B5026, at the Staffordshire boundary. After recording several bridges of uncertain parentage here is one definitely designed by Thomas Stanton on Telford's behalf. Stanton reported, in October 1829, that the existing bridge, consisting of two freestone arches of nine feet span, must be rebuilt as soon as possible. The drawing dated 1830, shows a twenty-two feet span masonry arch, faced with ornamental voussoirs with stepped extrados. The specification states that the whole is to be built of ashlar masonry, that is, smooth dressed stone in courses of not less than twelve inches depth. George E. Hamilton, Civil Engineer, of Wolverhampton built the bridge, the completion date being the 30th November 1830. It survives entirely as it was built.

The Newport - Whitchurch road, A41, crosses the Bailey Brook, a tributary of the Tern, five miles South of Whitchurch, at SANDFORD Bridge. This is an ashlar masonry bridge with ornamental arch facing rings with stepped extrados, comparable with Bearstone Bridge, the span being fourteen feet. About a hundred years ago the road over the bridge was widened, the widened portion being carried on plate girders. No historical records of the construction or the widening survive.

Three miles North West of Wem the Wem - Welshampton road, B5063, crosses the Whixall Brook, a tributary of the River Roden, at WOLVERLEY Bridge, a pleasing dressed sandstone structure. In August 1823 Thomas Stanton reported that the existing Wolverley Bridge consisted of two square openings, each four feet wide, the road being carried on flat sandstone slabs, each spanning four feet. He believed that the deteriorating slabs could be propped up for the coming winter, but after that the bridge would have to be replaced. He prepared a drawing, early in 1824, showing a seventeen feet span segmental arch bridge, to provide a more adequate waterway, with projecting ornamental voussoirs and stepped extrados, all in ashlar masonry. Parapets are shown as consisting of a single course, three feet six inches high, thicker at the bottom than at the top. The blocks forming the parapets were to be dowelled and leaded together. The bridge was completed, as designed, by November 1824 and remains in that form. This bridge was sited so as to provide an improved road line.

Following down the River Roden, past Spendford Bridge, which will be dealt with later, the next Telford bridge carries the Shrewsbury - Wem road, B5476, over the river at WEM, near Wem Mill. Here Thomas Stanton produced a drawing showing a twenty-four feet span segmental masonry arch bridge, with its abutment foundations supported on double plank platforms, resting on four feet timber piles, at two feet centres. John Simpson submitted a tender to build the proposed bridge, based on an estimate prepared by his assistant, John Lawrence. The tender was for £719 10s 0d if the ground was good enough to support the foundations without piles, and £737 10s 0d if piles were found to be necessary. The Justices awarded the contract to Simpson and the bridge was completed in 1808. Whether it was with or without the piles is not recorded.

Two miles below Wem the Roden is joined, from the North, by the Soulton Brook which passes under the Wem - Prees Green road, B5065, shortly before the confluence. Here, SOULTON Bridge, a red sandstone ashlar masonry segmental arch bridge of sixteen feet span is a pleasing and well proportioned structure. The finish of the bridge reflects the meticulously prepared drawing by Thomas Stanton for Telford. The builder who maintained Stanton's standards is not known. Here the wing wall foundations were to be carried down to the level of those for the abutments and built on an extension of the plank platform instead of making the wing wall foundations rather shallower. To provide for a deepening of the brook the abutments were underpinned in concrete in 1969.

The minor road from Wem to Lee Brockhurst crosses the Roden about a mile from Lee Brockhurst at THISTLEFORD Bridge. This eighteen feet span arch bridge of dressed sandstone was built by local subscription in 1796, though no records survive regarding the construction. By March 1844 Edward Haycock, the County Surveyor at that time, reported on the dangers arising from the inadequacy of the parapets which were only one foot six inches high. He proposed that "Scabbled red sandstone from Hawkstone Quarry" should be used to raise the height of the parapets a couple of feet. Having obtained the authority of the Justices to have the work carried out, he was able to issue a certificate authorizing payment for satisfactory work in December of that year.

The next bridge, following down the Roden, is at Lee Brockhurst where the

Lee Bridge. Due to the steepness of the approaches this bridge was a serious hazard to traffic. It was by-passed by a modern concrete bridge in 1962.

Shrewsbury - Whitchurch road, A49, at one time crossed over it by LEE Bridge, now by-passed by a pre-stressed concrete structure. This is a neat example of a single span, dressed red sandstone bridge of the period, the span being thirty six feet. The voussoirs of the facing ring are chamfered and there is a prominent keystone. The parapets and string course rise to a slight peak at midspan and there are pilasters at the abutment ends and at the ends of the curved wing walls. The spandrels are in the form of inset panels. The surviving drawing showing the bridge as built is undated and unsigned. I have no doubt, however, that it was prepared in Telford's office. He used the design again, with the span reduced to thirty feet for the bridge at Ryton, South of Shifnal, as we shall see. Here at Lee Bridge both approaches ran steeply downhill to the bridge which formed a double bend in the road and became a serious traffic hazzard. In 1825 the Lee Brockhurst Turnpike Trust complained of the difficulties of maintaining the road under these circumstances. Thomas Stanton investigated and commented that "The bridge was built by the County in 1800, since when no expenditure has been made for its maintenance or for that of the road". The Trust agreed to put things right to the tune of £60. He further reported on 21st April 1827 that the work had been well done. Nevertheless the road over the bridge continued to be the scene of numerous accidents, with the parapets frequently knocked into the river, until the diversion over the concrete bridge was built in 1962.

A mile and a half downstream from Lee Bridge at the first of two old Roden water mills, is HARCOURT MILL Bridge. It consists of two semicircular stone

Stanton Mill Bridge as it looked in 1940. The date stone marked 1790 and the parapet railings were incorporated in the new bridge in 1969 when this lovely old bridge was damaged beyond repair by floods. (Photo. A. Blackwall).

arches of about twelve feet span each but is of unknown date. It had become a County responsibility by 1872 and a report at that time states that it was built before the Bridge Repairs Act of 1803. It is quite likely to have been built at the same time as the next mill bridge, half a mile further downstream at Stanton-upon-Hine Heath. Here STANTON MILL Bridge was built with a date stone marked 1790. This was a segmental arch bridge of very broad and shallow voussoirs twenty feet in span. The parapets consisted of one course of masonry two feet deep, rising to a peak with the date stone at midspan. To make the parapets a safe height, doubtless following a stern rebuke from Thomas Stanton, little wrought iron railings were added on top of the stonework. In 1941 the arch, which had never been very strong, started to give trouble and a concrete saddle was laid over it to provide additional strength. However, in 1969 a rapid flood resulting from local storms resulted in the arch being damaged beyond repair. A prestressed concrete structure of simple design was built to replace it. This incorporated, with surprising success, the original stone and wrought iron parapets, including the ornamental date stone.

Another Eastern tributary of the River Tern is the River Pipe Strine which is spanned by a semicircular brick arch bridge of about twenty feet span known as RODWAY Bridge, a mile South of the village of Cherrington. The bridge is of no particular merit and no records exist of its construction or subsequent history. It is probable that it belongs to the period at present under consideration and is a comparatively rare local example of a brick bridge of that era.

Returning to the River Tern a substantial stone arch bridge of forty-one feet span may be found at LONGDON-ON-TERN, carrying the High Ercall - Shawbirch road, B5063. It appears that by 1792 a new bridge was required over the Tern at this point. An unsigned drawing was prepared showing a tastefully embellished stone arch bridge of thirty-six feet span. John Simpson of Shrewsbury contracted to build it for £630 in 1792. This contract was never executed but in 1795 Simpson did build a timber bridge over the Tern at this point and another one, over the mill stream a short distance down the road towards Shawbirch. We shall see more of the latter crossing later. The timber bridge over the Tern appears to have stood for about fifteen years, when again a new bridge was required. This time Thomas Stanton prepared the design, signed by Thomas Telford, and drew up the specification. The design was for a forty-one feet span segmental stone arch bridge of straightforward shape and proportions, in red sandstone. The construction, according to the design and specification, was completed in 1811, probably by John Simpson and so it survives to this day.

By 1812 the timber bridge over the mill stream, built in 1795, was due for replacement. It was known as LONG MILL Bridge, the mill being the property of Earl Gower, later to become the Duke of Sutherland and for some reason the County had become responsible for the mill bridge. For the construction of the new bridge a cast-iron arch was agreed upon and John Simpson submitted a quotation for building the stonework of the abutments and wing walls. The Coalbrookdale Company and William Hazledine entered competing quotations for casting and erecting the cast-iron arch and deck. Hazledine was successful with the lower figure of £206 14s 0d, though he was finally paid £230, the amount of the Coalbrookdale quotation. This iron bridge was completed by the end of 1812, the span being twenty-eight feet and the width of roadway thirteen feet. The County Surveyor in 1847, Edward Haycock, commented on the inadequate width of the bridge and set out a proposal to widen the structure by lengthening both abutments and providing an extra arch rib and deck. This work was carried out shortly after by George Snook.

Thomas Groves, the County Surveyor, in 1882, described the bridge as "A cast-iron bridge, having five arch ribs from which radiating uprights spring and support the upper ribs, upon which iron plates (are supported) and the roadway is formed". He went on to say that there were eight cracks in the ribs and nine in the spandrel columns. He had hoped to fishplate all these fractures but eventually had to accept that the general deterioration had gone too far and so prepared the design for a new bridge. This consisted of two lattice through-girders which formed the parapets and at the same time were the main bearers. (Hence the term through-girder). The original abutments were incorporated, £92 10s 0d being paid to Marshall Bros. of Shrewsbury for modifying the stonework. The wrought iron girders and deck were provided and erected by the Coalbrookdale Company for £270. It was completed in 1883 and demolished when the mill stream was filled in, in 1953. No trace now remains.

[The South and West]

The Shrewsbury - Montgomery road, B4386, crosses the Rowley Brook, a tributary of the Rea Brook, in Brockton, a hamlet almost joining on to the West end of the village of Worthen. BROCKTON Bridge consists of two blue brick arches on rubble masonry abutments. The parapets and wing walls are also of rubble. It is hardly an outstanding bridge though its listing as a structure of historic or architectural interest may be due to its place in a group of buildings in the locality. Be that as it may, the drabness of the blue brick arches is relieved by the inclusion of dressed masonry keystones. Before 1829 there was probably a ford here with maybe a footbridge. The Trustees of the Westbury - Montgomery Turnpike proposed to build a bridge of two eight feet spans which they hoped the County would take over. Thomas Stanton considered this waterway inadequate for winter flows and recommended two twelve feet spans. This was endorsed by Telford. Stanton also pointed out that the Shropshire Justices had decreed, in 1826, that no bridge less than eighteen feet wide would be taken over. The recommendations were accepted by the Trustees and the bridge was built by H. Hinks of Minsterley in 1829 and taken over by the County. Its width was nineteen feet and it has never been widened.

The Stapleton Brook, a tributary of the Cound Brook, passes under the Shrewsbury - Ludlow road, A49, at WAYFORD Bridge, five miles South of Shrewsbury. In 1811 Thomas Stanton wrote to Joseph Loxdale, the Clerk of the Peace, to say that he had examined the old two span bridge which was there then

Church Bridge, Dorrington, carries what was once the Dorrington-Condover-Atcham Turnpike over the Cound Brook. (Photo. A. Blackwall).

38

and that, in his opinion, it was beyond repair and a new bridge was required. He enclosed a drawing and specifications of the structure he proposed. This showed a segmental stone arch bridge of twenty-four feet span, all in fine dressed stone. The parapets and string course are shown slightly cambered and the wing walls curved. The width of the roadway is shown as eighteen feet. The specification stated that the new bridge was to be built on the same site as the old one. The abutment foundations were to be on a double layer of oak planking, each layer three inches thick and the bottom layer to be three feet below bed level. Details of the masonry are set out, it was to be "Chisel draft and pointed, the stones to be procured from Condover Quarry, belonging to the Rev. Archdeacon Corbet, near the point of the Lawley". John Simpson submitted the only tender which was for £553. Work was probably completed in 1812. It was widened by extending the arch in reinforced concrete incorporated with the re-use of the external masonry in the 1920s.

A poster of 1828 offers two guineas reward for information "Regarding the throwing down of coping stones (from the parapet of Wayford Bridge) as will be the means of convicting the person or persons who have damaged the bridge".

Immediately South of Wayford Bridge is the village of Dorrington from which the minor road to Condover was once the Dorrington - Condover - Atcham Turnpike. The dressed red sandstone bridge, of a twenty-four feet main arch and two small flood arches, known as CHURCH Bridge, was built to carry the turnpike over the Cound Brook. No record of its history can be found though it is known to have been in existence in 1822.

The scene now moves to the old Shrewsbury - Bishops Castle Turnpike, which ran via Longden, Pulverbatch, Wentnor and More. This crosses the Kinnerton Brook a mile and a half North of Wentnor, over a nine feet span arch bridge built by George Edgecombe of Ellesmere in 1833. Major repairs may have been carried out to the bridge fifty years later. A minor road joins it from the East, at this point, after crossing the River East Onny over a rubble masonry bridge of twelve feet span. The parapets are topped by alternate large and small jagged stones, known as "Cock and Hen" coping as at Clun. Both these small bridges appear to have the name, ASHGROVE and they have also been referred to as GRAVENOR.

Five miles down the old turnpike towards Bishops Castle the West branch of the River Onny is crossed by NEWTON Bridge, South of the village of More. Here the local community decided to replace the bridge, having been charged with permitting its dilapidation, by the County Magistrates. Thomas Stanton duly sent them a drawing of a suitable structure. This shows a bridge of two fourteen feet span segmental arches with a central pier whose foundations, like those of the abutments, are at a depth of four feet below bed level. The approach roads are raised safely above possible flood level and provide a gentle climb onto the bridge. The community's spokesman, a local J.P., wrote to the Clerk of the Peace on 27th March 1813, saying "On Thursday I received from Mr. Stanton a plan for building the bridge . . . . which is too absurd for us to attempt to erect. I do not apprehend that it is necessary for the Surveyor General to give his opinion as to what sort of bridge should be built . . . . We sent at your request a plan for the bridge . . . . which we could have completed at one third of the expense of the plan proposed by Mr. Stanton". He intended to inform Lord Powys of the situation. The latter plan to which the J.P. referred had apparently been prepared locally by Herbert Oakley. His drawing shows a bridge of three arches, one of twelve feet and two of eight feet. The approach roads climb very steeply from just above water level to a sharp hump at midspan. No foundation details are shown. Telford's comments to the Clerk of the Peace were that the plan, drawn by Mr. Oakley would, in fact, involve the County in unnecessary expense and he would be failing in his duty if he recommended it. He was convinced that Mr. Oakley's inexperience in such matters had led him to the conclusions that he had drawn. Approaches should not be steeper than one in twenty-four, for the sake of the horses; low lying approaches would be subject to frequent flooding; the lack of information about depth of foundations was a serious omission and he did not feel he could recommend such a departure from Stanton's basic design. However, if the County Magistrates thought it proper to authorize a bridge to Mr. Oakley's plan they were, of course at liberty to do so. By December 1815 the bridge was completed. Telford went down to More to inspect it and showed a high degree of forbearance and fairmindedness by reporting "It is built of rubble stone and apparently of good workmanship. As to the perfections of the foundations and interior work (which I, of course, had no opportunity of examining) it is vouchsafed for by a respectable Magistrate. I can therefore see no reason why it should not be admitted as a County Bridge".

The bridge which has survived bears little resemblance to Mr. Oakley's drawing except for the dimensions of the three arches. In other respects the stonemason had used his judgement and followed Stanton's design except that he apparently ignored the depth of foundations, in spite of the fact that they were "vouchsafed for by a respectable Magistrate". The result was that some years later Stanton had to report that he had arranged to fence off the part of the bridge that had collapsed due to the river undercutting the foundations and would execute repairs and re-establish foundations at an adequate depth. The bridge was widened quite tastefully in 1934. It has been suggested that Mr. Oakley's original conception of the bridge was inspired by that depicted on Willow Pattern china which had been recently introduced by the Caughley China Works, near Coalport and was no doubt popular in the district at this time.

The road leading from the turnpike at Newton Bridge, into the village of More, crosses the West branch of the Onny over MORE Bridge. This is a neat little rubble masonry bridge with dressed stone facing rings and prominent keystones. The coping of the parapets is of dressed flat stones rising to a peak at midspan. As the span is less than fifteen feet and provides barely half the waterway at Newton Bridge, the next crossing, and in addition the width is only twelve feet, it is most unlikely that it was built under County direction. The pleasing proportions and lines of this little bridge remain as a credit to some unknown designer and the building resources of More village. It did eventually become a County Bridge in 1931.

In 1820 the Borough of Bishops Castle was an important country town which returned two M.P.s to Parliament. However its highway connection with the busy turnpike between Shrewsbury and Ludlow was not satisfactory and a trust was set up to construct a turnpike road, running due East from Bishops Castle to Plowden, then following the North bank of the River Onny to the Southern end of the village of Wistanstow, where it joined the Shrewsbury - Ludlow road. This called for a crossing of the Onny on the Choulton side of Plowden, now known as CHOULTON Bridge. The Trust approached Telford who, as a part-time employee of the County was available for private contract work, to prepare surveys, plans, specification and estimate of cost for the bridge. The intention was, of course, that the bridge should be such that the County would take it over. Telford's fee was £8 17s 6d and a snecked rubble masonry bridge, of thirty feet span, eighteen feet wide, was completed by 1826. A river training wall was added on the downstream side and it became a County Bridge in 1828.

The Shrewsbury - Ludlow road, A49, crosses the River Onny, over what is officially known as GROVE Bridge, though sometimes referred to as STREFFORD Bridge, half a mile South of Wistanstow. Jervoise quotes John Leland as having noted a stone bridge at "Whister" in the early 1500s. In 1826 Thomas Stanton reported that the existing bridge had been built in a very superficial and imperfect manner with too little waterway and was inconveniently narrow. At that time the crossing was a little upstream of the site of the present bridge and the turnpike ran straight into the village and then made its way towards Shrewsbury. Stanton prepared plans and a specification for a new bridge, with a road alignment roughly as it is now. A temporary timber bridge was required during construction. The cost of this and the permanent bridge was estimated at £1500. The drawing shows a single masonry arch bridge of forty feet span. Foundations are shown at ten feet below the springing level of the arch and are supported on two layers of timber planks. The width is shown as twenty feet. In fact the drawing shows the bridge as it stands today, except for the steel footbridge which is now alongside it.

The contract to build Grove Bridge was awarded to Matthew Stead and William Slack of Ludlow, the completion date being set as 13th November 1828. Work started with the stone being got from the quarry at Cheney Longville but Stanton was soon unhappy about the way it was proceeding. He was also concerned that the temporary bridge was very inferior to what was shown in the drawings. On one visit he was accompanied by Telford who wrote, the same day, that he had seen much to concern him. Neither of the contractors was on site and the men were dressing unsuitable stone. He was very critical of the temporary bridge and felt that with their present attitude the contractors would never finish on time. Stanton suggested a full-time overseer in the capacity Matthew Davidson, occupied at Montford. Stanton himself had to commute from his office at Ellesmere, more than thirty miles away, to visit the works. A couple of months later he was able to report that he found the work proceeding in a workmanlike manner, agreeable to the plans and specification, under the watchful eye of the overseer "recommended by Mr. Telford". He felt, however, that the work was still "much backwarder than it ought to have been", resulting in the contractors receiving another shake up. The result of their labours was

41

nevertheless a substantial structure which still carries the Trunk Road traffic.

A mile down the road, in the middle of Craven Arms, the B4368 road leads off, North Eastwards towards Much Wenlock. As soon as the houses of Craven Arms are left behind this road crosses the River Onny by a lattice through-girder bridge, called CLUNSFORD Bridge, which we shall deal with later in its proper place. The bridge which preceded it was a masonry structure of two twenty-four feet span segmental arches designed and supervised by Stanton in 1834. It survived for just over fifty years.

Seven miles along the B4368 from Craven Arms, up the valley of the River Corve, is the hamlet of Millichope. The lane leading off to the right, towards Tugford crosses the Corve by BEAMBRIDGE, a twenty feet span rubble masonry arch bridge. In 1810 the inhabitants of the Franchise of Wenlock were charged with failing to maintain the bridge on this site. Their defence was that as far back in 1693 the people of the parish of Tugford had been held responsible. However the legal situation was settled and a contract was awarded to John Smallman to build a new bridge to his own design for £160. His design was approved by Telford in February 1811 and the construction of the bridge was successfully completed.

The next turning to the right, off the B4368, also leads to Tugford, crossing the Corve by BROADSTONE Bridge. This is a rubble masonry arch bridge of twenty feet span rather similar to Beambridge and may be contemporary with it. The upstream parapet has "cock and hen" coping while the downstream one is capped with a mortar coping which probably encloses a "cock and hen" layout, making it more comfortable to sit on while fishing the Corve.

Coming back down the B4368, from Broadstone towards Craven Arms but turning left at the Pedlar's Rest and down the B4365, towards Bromfield the village of Stanton Lacy, lying on the far side of the Corve, is reached about a mile short of the A49. The side road leading into Stanton Lacy crosses the river on a lattice through-girder bridge, built in 1878 and dealt with in Chapter 5. Here, in 1821 Thomas Stanton was concerned about the condition of the three span rubble masonry bridge then carrying the road and suggested rebuilding it for an estimated £150. However he or Telford was attracted by a design, prepared by Matthew Stead of Ludlow, for a single arch bridge in rubble masonry and he drew up a specification covering the design. He modified the wing wall layout, in pencil, on Stead's drawing and returned it to him with a letter accepting the design subject to the pencilled alterations. This bridge was completed in 1826 and stood for fifty-two years, until the present bridge was built. Matthew Stead's plan with Stanton's alterations in pencil, survives.

BROMFIELD Bridge, carrying the A49 over the River Onny is a modern, prestressed concrete bridge, built in 1969 to replace the earlier three span, rubble masonry bridge. This earlier structure was built after complaints about the dangerous state of its ancient predecessor. Thomas Stanton produced a design for Telford in May 1811. This shows three segmental stone arches, the centre one having a span of thirty-six feet and the other two thirty-two feet each. The ends of the midstream piers are shown as half columns terminating just above the springing level, though in the bridge, as built, the half columns continued up to the parapet coping and were decorated with a cruciform loophole motif. John Straphen of Shrewsbury undertook to build the bridge for £2,015, the completion date being the 1st November 1812. Stanton's specification called for the backs of the arches to be covered with punned clay, for waterproofing, and for Parker's Cement to be used for pointing joints in the masonry.

Just South of Craven Arms the A49 crosses the River Onny over the present bridge, built in 1968-69, consisting of pre-flexed beams of high tensile steel enclosed in and decked with concrete. Known as STOKESAY Bridge, because of its proximity to Stokesay Castle, this structure replaced a Telford iron bridge which became unsafe for modern traffic in 1965. The old iron bridge was first replaced in situ, by a Callendar - Hamilton emergency bridge. This is a warren truss girder bridge which was constructed as a matter of extreme urgency, working day and night because the trunk road was closed to traffic. The method used was to build the warren girders at high level over the top of the old bridge. The girder bridge was then jacked down until its ends coincided with the existing road level. While this was being done the old bridge was dismantled and the pieces carefully removed and returned to the Coalbrookdale Works from which they had originated.

Turning back the clock to the time of the construction of the iron Stokesay Bridge, we find that on New Year's Day 1822 Thomas Stanton was called out to make the long and uncomfortable journey from his Ellesmere office to Stokesay as quickly as he possibly could. It is to be hoped that the New Year celebrations of the previous evening had not been too convivial. He arrived at the site to find the predecessor of the iron bridge ". . . completely washed down and a new one must be erected. The position of this bridge has always been precarious due to the weir". The weir, which is still there, serves an estate water supply. Work started immediately on the preparation of drawings for the construction of a cast-iron bridge. In fact he decided that he could use a design he had already used twice, once at Meole Brace and once at Cound. As we have not discussed either of these bridges we will describe the design here. The span was fifty-five feet and the deck plates were supported on four cast-iron arch ribs. Each rib was cast in two halves, each consisting of the arch rib and the deck beam above it, with the spandrel framing supporting the beam all cast in one piece, presenting an elegant elevation. Authority was given by the Justices at the 1822 Easter Sessions for work to proceed. The Coalbrookdale Company won the contract to provide and erect the ironwork for £525 and John Straphen the contract for the masonry, using stone from Long Lane or Onibury Quarry. According to the plate on the bridge it was completed in 1823. A hundred years later a number of fractures developed in the two inner ribs and these were encased in reinforced concrete to the design of L. G. Mouchel and Partners. For some years prior to the closure of the bridge the parapets were so frequently subject to damage from traffic that an arrangement was made with the Atlas Foundry in Shrewsbury whereby duplicate diagrams of the parapets, with the panels numbered, were kept in the Bridge Office and at the Foundry. So that as soon as damage was reported the Bridge Engineer was able to telephone the Foundry and give the numbers of the panels for which replacements were required.

Dinham Bridge, Ludlow, guarded by the impressive ruins of Ludlow Castle.

As the old A49 road enters Ludlow, from the North, it is joined on the East side by the Bewdley - Ludlow road, A4117, which, at this point has just crossed the River Corve by the fine ashlar sandstone OLD CORVE Bridge of three arches, the centre one of twenty feet and the other two of seventeen feet. I have been able to find no record of its construction or other history but understand that it replaced an earlier stone bridge probably towards the end of the eighteenth century.

The minor road running Westwards out of Ludlow towards the Whitcliffe and Bringewood Chase, crosses the River Teme immediately below the Castle, on an impressive structure of three lofty arches constructed, like the rest of the bridge, of rubble masonry. This is DINHAM Bridge. There are half columns above the cutwaters reminiscent of old Bromfield Bridge suggesting that Stanton was behind its construction, but there is no record beyond the date, 1825. Jervoise quotes William Stukeley who says in his *Itinerarium Curiosum* of 1721, that in his time there was a timber bridge on stone piers at Dinham.

Two miles South of Ludlow, just beyond Ashford Hall, a road leads off the A49 Eastwards towards Clee Hill. After the railway it crosses the River Teme on a beautifully proportioned single arch bridge of eighty-one feet span, with numerous little flood arches under the approaches. This is ASHFORD Bridge, designed by Telford himself. He decided, for the first time, to reduce the weight at the quarter span points by making the spandrels hollow. The specification (no drawing survives) lays down that ". . . internal parts of the spandrels to be secured by culverts or brick walls with proper covering stones". The extrados of the arch was waterproofed with three inches of lime mortar, in this case, instead of clay. That it was quite ineffective as a waterproofing agent we shall see in due course. It was an age of experiment and, as we say today "You can't win them all". Contracts were signed with William Atkins, Stonemason and Thomas Smith, Carpenter, for the construction of the bridge for £830, to be completed by 25th November 1797. There is a date stone at midspan on the downstream side which confirms this. The source of stone for the arch voussoirs is not known but it can be seen that they consist almost alternatively of hard acidic gritstone and softer alkaline limestone. The result, over the years, is the progressive erosion of the limestone as water finds its way through the arch. In 1970 all the stonework was repaired, impregnated and sealed with various silicone solutions to prevent further decay. A waterproof surface was laid all over the bridge, at road level, to prevent ingress of water there. Water is perhaps the most destructive agent of bridges. A cast-iron plate, fixed to the parapet, states that earlier major repairs had been carried out under Thomas Groves, County Surveyor, in 1877. Surprisingly the brick parapets and pilasters are original and not modifications at the time of that repair.

Over Ashford Bridge, a couple of miles towards Clee Hill, the Ledwyche Brook is crossed at CAYNHAM Bridge. An earlier bridge on this site had been built in 1780 but according to Stanton, the waterway provided by it was inadequate and, by 1821 damage by flooding and scour made a new bridge necessary. He drew out the plans for a thirty-five feet span segmental stone arch bridge to be built a little way upstream of the older one. The contract for building this very solid looking structure was awarded to John Straphen and work was completed by February 1824, for £676.

The B4385 road from Bishops Castle to Leintwardine crosses the River Clun by BROADWARD Bridge, a mile South of Clungunford. Here in 1831 the County was charged with the neglect of the old bridge. Thomas Stanton duly prepared the design for a bridge of two segmental stone arches of twenty-seven feet six inches span each. He proposed a well finished structure with stepped extrados on the ornamental facing rings of the arches. Stone was specified from Shelderton Quarry, a mile or so away to the East and the timber for the foundation grillage was to be beech or elm. Richard Jones of Bucknell contracted to build the bridge for £650.

[The South and East]

There is a minor road which leaves the A4117 at Cleobury Mortimer and runs South Westwards to Tenbury Wells. Two miles after leaving Cleobury Mortimer it crosses the Mill Brook at HAY Bridge (on some old maps it is marked as HIGH Bridge), a neat stone and brick structure of twenty-one feet span. Continuing down this road but turning off to the left towards Neen Sollars the brook is crossed again at MILLBROOK Bridge, a very similar bridge to the previous one, a stone and brick arch bridge of twenty feet span. Both are thought to have been built during the period of this chapter.

In Neen Sollars village there is a mellow brick bridge; one of the few so far considered, of two eighteen feet span arches. James Brown, on behalf of the parish, sent in to Shrewsbury a report from the Easter Sessions in 1834, concerning the river crossing existing at that time in the village. This was a three span timber bridge, sixty feet in length, over the River Rea, NEEN SOLLARS Bridge, built in about 1780. Mr. Brown described the village street in Neen Sollars, as part of the Bewdley - Tenbury Turnpike, possibly to influence the Justices towards taking over responsibility for the river crossing. The Bewdley - Tenbury road now, as then, crosses the Rea at Newnham Bridge in Worcestershire. If this was an attempt, on Mr. Brown's part, to impress it achieved little, for Joshua Peele, the Clerk of the Peace, replied that the parish must repair or replace the old bridge and could not discharge themselves from further liability by so doing. It could never, he said, become a County Bridge. In fact, it did not become a County Bridge until the general take over of District Council Bridges in 1931. To return to the construction of Neen Sollars Bridge; nothing daunted, Mr. Brown then asked for the design requirements for a highway bridge. The reply was "Mr. Telford, the County Surveyor, or his assistant, Mr. Stanton of Ellesmere would provide the information". This was in July 1834 and only a matter of weeks before Telford's death and there is no record of the production of the design or its acceptance. However it is recorded that the indefatigable Mr. Brown undertook the task of raising the necessary funds from local residents and even setting up a kiln and making the bricks. The bridge for which he was responsible still stands as a monument to his efforts though one parapet has been replaced by one of rubble masonry. When the situation arose there was no-one who was prepared to have a go at manufacturing some matching bricks.

The road from Bridgnorth to Cleobury Mortimer, now the B4363, has always been one of some importance and was certainly a well used turnpike in Telford's time. Its route crosses a number of brooks in deep valleys, presenting a variety of bridge approach problems. These problems exercised the mind and energies of Thomas Stanton and his reports constitute, in many cases the earliest recorded mention of the existence of the bridges concerned. In 1825 Stanton worked his way down the road, from Bridgnorth, repairing, reconstructing, widening and raising the level of the roadway over each bridge so as to ease the steep gradients of the approaches. First, MARLBROOK Bridge, over the Mor Brook, consisting of two fourteen feet spans of dressed stone, was dealt with. It is now a listed structure. Secondly, GLAZELEY Bridge, a thirteen feet span stone arch bridge was treated in the same way. At a more recent date it has been further widened on the downstream side, supported on a steel and concrete beam. Next, HORSEFORD Bridge had its roadway raised as much as seven feet to ease the gradient from the North but it was not widened until quite recently. PRIORS MOOR Bridge, referred to by Stanton as FRIARS MOOR, was not raised but was widened to eighteen feet between parapets. WALLTOWN Bridge, a seven feet six inches span stone culvert with deep spandrels was raised by nine feet six inches, making it a very high structure and necessitating the addition of buttresses to stabilize the lofty retaining walls. In the 1960s the arch was found to be in a ruinous condition and was lined with a reinforced concrete tube.

Finally Cleobury Mortimer Bridge, known as NEW BRIDGE, completes the run of bridges between this town and Bridgnorth. New Bridge is a lofty masonry arch bridge of forty feet span, widened in the 1930s by extending the arch in reinforced concrete and providing new stone facing for the widened side. There is a legal document concerning liability for the repair of a bridge, on this site, in 1789. As Thomas Telford was still working on his own at this time the drawings and contract documents required by the situation are presumably from his hand. The drawing shows an arch of forty feet span and fourteen feet rise, the width between parapets being fifteen feet. The facing of the arch, which is two feet thick, is shown with projecting, chamfered voussoirs. Flood openings through the wing walls, immediately behind the abutments, are shown on the drawing but were apparently abandoned in the construction. The construction contract, for £450, signed by Telford and Thos. Smallman, builder, of Worcester, is dated 13th October 1792. The bridge was reported to be in some trouble by 1815 (when Telford would have been busy with the improvement of the Holyhead Road for the Parliamentary Commission and preparations for the Waterloo Bridge at Bettws-y-Coed). The matter was shelved until 1825 when, in the spring, Stanton drew up a specification for the strengthening of the bridge with buttresses and wrought iron tie bars through the spandrels. At the same time the roadway was to be raised by four feet. A contract was made with John Provis to carry out the work for £210. It is difficult now to see how much of this work was carried out owing to the modern widening. Correspondence suggests that Provis objected to having to accept a seven year maintenance guarantee but there is no evidence of it having been modified for him.

At the same time as the work on the Bridgnorth - Cleobury Mortimer road bridges Stanton carried out similar operations on the bridges carrying the Bridgnorth - Ludlow road, now the B4364. This particularly applies to the eleven feet span stone arch bridge at WALLSBATCH. The twenty-four feet span stone arch bridge at Middleton was subsequently reconstructed in reinforced concrete in 1937. Harpswood Bridge, carrying the B4364 over the Mor brook, and which has already been mentioned in Chapter 1, received considerable attention at this time.

[The East]

To find the remainder of the bridges in Shropshire, built during Telford's time as County Surveyor, we should start once again from Shrewsbury following the Ludlow road, out of the town. At Meole Brace this road now crosses the Rea Brook by a reinforced concrete bridge, built in 1933 which also carries the A5 Shrewsbury By-pass. The previous MEOLE BRACE Bridge, of course only carried the Ludlow road. In 1788 the Borough of Shrewsbury invited proposals for improving the crossing of the Rea Brook at Meole Brace. It was then a very narrow stone bridge of four spans. Telford wrote his comments on the proposals received: that of Carline and Tilley was too narrow at fifteen feet, as was John

Turnbull's; Mr. Nelson's was the best but fell short in "not expressing the direction of the road at each end". He decided to carry out the work himself and produced a drawing showing the old bridge widened to eighteen feet. This was carried out but by 1811 the widened bridge had become unsatisfactory in some way and Thomas Stanton produced the design for a cast-iron bridge of fifty-five feet span. John Simpson was awarded the contract for building the stonework and William Hazledine overcame some competition from Coalbrookdale to obtain the contract for providing the ironwork. The bridge was completed in 1811 but much work was also carried out on the diversion of the Rea Brook and the Mill Brook. That the old stone bridge had failed is suggested by the fact that Carline and J. H. Haycock were engaged to build a temporary timber bridge, for use until the new bridge was complete. Failure of the old bridge would most likely have been caused by foundation scour, due to flood water approaching it at an awkward angle. To avoid a repetition of this was, no doubt, the reason for the diversion of the two brooks. Nevertheless by 1824 Stanton was reporting fresh river flow problems. In spite of these the 1811 bridge survived until 1933, and was demolished then only because of the construction of the by-pass.

In 1818, seven years after the completion of Meole Brace Bridge, Thomas Stanton had a second use for the design used at Meole Brace (little knowing that he would be glad to use it a third time, four years later, at Stokesay, where we have described it in detail). Now the design was to be used to build COUND Bridge, over the Cound Brook, half a mile North of the village of Cound, to carry the Shrewsbury - Much Wenlock road, A458. In 1795 John Dodson contracted to build a bridge at this point, to his own design. He built a cast-iron arch bridge of thirty-six feet span, twelve feet wide. With the Cound Brook's propensity for sudden flooding at that time, the span was apparently inadequate and in 1818 Telford was ordered by the Justices to prepare designs and estimates for an adequate replacement. The fifty-five feet span, cast-iron arch, designed for Meole Brace bridge would comfortably provide the required enlargement of the waterway. The design had proved successful and so could well be used again. John Carline was awarded the contract to carry out the stonework of the abutments and wing walls and William Hazledine that for the ironwork, having successfully competed with Richard Darby of Coalbrookdale for it. Carline's was not a happy contract for some reason. The temporary bridge was built, as required, but it provided a "hazardous crossing" and was a constant source of complaint. This was aggravated by delays to the completion of the permanent work by the discovery of running sand, that deadly enemy of sound foundations. He became the recipient of abusive anonymous letters and the dressed stone facing of the abutments, as they were completed, was maliciously defaced. He was compelled to appeal to the Justices for financial assistance from County funds. The bridge was however completed eventually and gave good service until the early 1920s when the inner arch ribs started to break up and were encased in reinforced concrete, as at Stokesay. In 1967 cracks in the concrete prompted the decision to replace the bridge and the present pre-stressed concrete structure was then built. The outer ribs were preserved intact in the demolition and given to the National Trust for erection as an ornamental footbridge in Attingham Park. For financial reasons they were not used for this purpose and were eventually moved to the Ironbridge Gorge Museum Trust's site at Blists Hill where they are stored pending the location of a site for them. During the building of the concrete bridge at Cound in 1967 running sand once more presented serious problems in the establishment of the foundations.

In addition to Meole Brace, Cound and Stokesay there was an indirect use for the Meole Brace iron arch design, in 1813. The Cound Brook flows under the Shrewsbury - Acton Burnell road near Cantlop. CANTLOP Bridge is of cast-iron and, in a way, is a miniature of Meole Brace, using a curtailed form of the arch ribs, the span being thirty-one feet. Unlike Cound and Stokesay however it was never strengthened with reinforced concrete and is still in its original form. For many years historians refused to connect the bridge with Telford and dismissed it as being of little historical importance. However close inspection for maintenance purposes showed that the details of design must have originated from Meole Brace Bridge. Eventually it became accepted and was scheduled as an Ancient Monument. It is now the sole surviving example of a Telford cast-iron arch highway bridge in the County. It appears that the County considered taking over a bridge, on this site, in 1812 but found that it required strengthening and widening. A new bridge appeared to be the best solution. Some years later, in 1831, Joshua Peele, then the Deputy Clerk of the Peace, wrote to Telford's office to enquire whether the cast-iron bridge, erected by subscription in 1813, had been built under his direction and to his satisfaction. Stanton replied that it

Cantlop Bridge, scheduled as an ancient monument, is the sole surviving example of a Telford cast-iron arch highway bridge in the County.

had. Whoever carried out the detail design, under Telford's direction, must have been loaned the Meole Brace Design to work from, if it was not Stanton.

In 1974 a passer-by telephoned the Shire Hall to say he had noticed a series of cracks in one of the cast-iron members of Cantlop Bridge. I immediately hurried to the site, as did Stanton to Stokesay in 1822, and was able to confirm some extremely fine but indisputable cracks in one of the arch ribs. A weight restriction was imposed straightaway and, with financial help from the Directorate of Ancient Monuments a permanent, pre-stressed concrete bridge was built, by-passing the cast-iron bridge which could then be preserved. A picnic site has been developed in the vicinity for visitors to the bridge. Some time later I obtained the identity of the passer-by who had called my attention to the fractures, thanked him and congratulated him on his keen eyesight, to have spotted what were only hair cracks. He then described the "cracks" he had seen which turned out to be, without any doubt, joints between the iron deck plates. Nevertheless his timely warning may well have prevented a disaster.

The Cound Brook is spanned about a quarter of a mile South of Cound Bridge by another cast-iron structure, COUND ARBOUR Bridge, of similar span to Cantlop. It bears no resemblance to it, however, the ribs here incorporate a spandrel frame consisting of a series of cast-iron rings diminishing in size towards midspan. The deck, formed of iron plates, follows the arched form of the rib, the roadway being carried on filling materials as in a masonry arch bridge. There was still much to be learned about the use of iron arches. In due course this filling material was removed and replaced with good quality concrete, forming a mass concrete arch and invisibly strengthening the bridge. A plate at midspan states that the ironwork was cast at Coalbrookdale in 1797. The motif in cast-iron rings diminishing in size may be seen on a number of other Coalbrookdale bridges in various parts of the world. It has been suggested that John Dodson, the builder of the first iron bridge at Cound, was responsible for Cound Arbour Bridge which was built by local subscription. There is no written evidence of this however.

In 1795 the flood which damaged a number of bridges over the Severn included, among its casualties, the old stone bridge of four Gothic arches, over the river near Buildwas Abbey. The Justices instructed Thomas Telford to initiate the necessary steps towards the construction of a new BUILDWAS Bridge. The Coalbrookdale Company submitted a design in the form of a scale model, based on the Iron Bridge, Telford had commented that the Iron Bridge was lacking in its resistance to the horizontal thrust from the earth pressure behind the abutments. Be that as it may, the Justices at first accepted the Coalbrookdale design. Telford submitted his own design. This consisted of ribs of comparatively flat curvature superimposed upon ribs of smaller radius. The flatter ribs were to counteract the earth pressure and the other ones to carry the weight, as in the case of Farnolls Pritchard's 1775 design for the Iron Bridge. Like Pritchard, Telford may have been influenced by the timber bridge over the River Rhine at Schaffhausen, at the time of its construction the longest bridge span in the world. The Justices were not impressed by his design but eventually agreed that the claims of the Coalbrookdale model and those of Telford's drawings should be arbitrated by a panel consisting of two ironmasters, with bridge building experience, John Wilkinson and William Reynolds. They chose Telford's design and he later wrote ". . . the bridge has been built of iron at the expense of the County, £6,444, from a plan given by me as County Surveyor. It was executed in a masterly manner by the (Coalbrookdale) Company and finished in 1796". The construction contract was placed with Richard Dearman of Coalbrookdale. During construction a temporary timber bridge of eight spans carried the highway traffic.

In 1887 the County Surveyor, Thomas Groves, reported on Buildwas Bridge to the Finance Committee "The bridge has arrived at a stage when more than superficial repair is required and this, looking at the material of which it is composed, and its age, is not to be wondered at. There is, I may say, some uncertainty exactly as to the proportions in which the weight is carried by the respective arches, and I believe must always be so in a transition structure of this nature, constructed before engineering had learned to rely entirely upon the adaption of cast-iron and wrought-iron to bridges of large span." The County decided to consult Sir John Fowler who said in a letter dated 2nd October 1888 ". . . having inspected the bridge there is nothing in my opinion calling for special action". Subsequent investigation suggests that over the eighty-two years that the bridge had been standing when Sir John Fowler examined it, gradual but massive earth movement, down the valley side had squeezed the abutments towards one another a distance of between two and three feet. By 1905 the movement had reached a point where the bridge had to be replaced.

The present Pratt truss steel girder bridge was then constructed by the Horsehay Company using, very largely, the original masonry abutments. The South end of this bridge is fixed while the North end rested on rollers to allow for thermal expansion and contraction. After twenty years the roller bearings were replaced by phosphor bronze and steel slides. But the movement was not only due to changes in temperature. The slides have to accommodate the movement, all in one direction, due to the earth pressure against the backs of the abutments. As this movement can be as much as an inch a year, by 1954 the slides had reached the limit of their travel and so were extended by a foot. In 1968 the limit of the slides was again reached. This time the bridge, which weighs four hundred tons, was moved towards the fixed end abutment, a distance of eighteen inches so that the slides could accommodate a further eighteen inches of earth movement. The method was to fabricate steel brackets and fix them to the fixed end of the girders. Hydraulic jacks were set as to lift the bridge *via* the brackets and greased plates were slipped in under that end of the bridge. The jacks were then moved to the other end of the bridge and set so as to push horizontally. In this way the bridge, sliding on the greased plates at one end and the slides at the other, was moved the required distance to give the slides their maximum movement once again. The fixed end then had to be lifted again to remove the greased plates and fix it to the top of the abutment once more. This was to give the bridge at least another twenty years of life.

The scene now moves to the upper waters of the River Worfe, near Shifnal. Following the Western branch of the river the first bridge encountered is at

EVELITH MILL, a mile and a half South of Shifnal. This rather ordinary brick bridge is included solely because the site was the setting for a situation of high drama in the escape of Prince Charles after the Battle of Worcester. As he crossed the Worfe, under the cover of darkness, the miller opened his door at the moment of the royal refugee's passing and raised the alarm. However sanctuary was found for the night in Madeley and the following night the escape continued back to the famous Boscobel Oak and eventually to safety in France. The bridge must have been a predecessor of the present one which was probably built in about 1800.

We now move across to the Eastern branch of the Worfe which passes under the Shifnal - Wolverhampton road, A464, at Cosford Pumping Station. The road now by-passes this COSFORD Bridge which is a segmental arch bridge of brick and stone, of twenty-four feet span and originally built in 1780. This road was once part of the famous Holyhead Road used by the Mail Coaches. The whole of the Mail Route from London to Holyhead was improved and reconstructed, at the behest of a Parliamentary Commission set up by the Post Master General in 1821. Telford was appointed in charge of the operation which included replacing or strengthening numerous bridges, including Cosford Bridge which was thus largely rebuilt under his direction in 1822. A report to the County Justices sometime after Telford's death claims the bridge to be of substantial construction and in good condition.

Returning to the Western branch of the river the next bridge dating from this period is at Grindle and is known as GRINDLEFORGE or OLD FORGE Bridge. This is quite an impressive structure but is, in fact, a solid causeway, more than a hundred yards long, across the valley floor and joining two small bridges, at either end, both of brick, faced with dressed sandstone masonry. Under the causeway itself are two four feet flood arches which could presumably be closed by sluices when the long field upstream was a huge mill pond, down the side of which the Worfe flowed, passing under the bridge at the West end of the causeway. In 1794 John Simpson rebuilt the walls of the causeway, making the parapet coping climb to a peak at the centre, giving the impression, on the road, of a very long bridge. All the stonework visible dates from John Simpson's rebuilding, though in 1841 Edward Haycock, the County Surveyor, described it as an ancient structure.

A mile further down the Worfe the river is spanned by a bridge carrying the main street of Ryton village. This is a single arch bridge of dressed red sandstone of thirty feet span. The voussoirs in the facing ring are chamfered and there is a prominent keystone. The parapet coping, string course and pilasters are well proportioned and finished. The whole impression is that of a duplicate of Lee Bridge, which suggests Telford's involvement and dates RYTON Bridge at about 1800.

A somewhat similar structure crosses the river another mile downstream. This is BECKBURY Bridge and is to the West of the village. Here the span is twenty-five feet and the voussoirs, though of red sandstone, are plain. The parapets, including coping and string course, have been completely removed and replaced by nine inch brick walls with rather nasty glazed ridge tiles as coping. This bridge was probably built from local resources, about the same time as Ryton Bridge. The slight differences in finish, from the other bridge, together with its rather inadequate width of twelve feet, suggests that it was not built under Telford's direction.

The line of the old Madeley - Dudley Turnpike leaves the Telford - Bridgnorth road, A442, just North of Sutton Maddock and runs in a South Easterly direction, crossing the Bridgnorth - Wolverhampton road, A454, at Upper Ludstone. This section of the old turnpike has been known locally for many years as the Rabbit Run. The lane which runs from the Rabbit Run into the village of Stableford crosses the Worfe by STABLEFORD Bridge. This is a dressed red sandstone arch bridge, the facing voussoirs being quite plain and with no keystone. The width is twelve feet. In fact this must be as Beckbury Bridge was before it had its parapets removed. For some reason it has been Listed as a Structure of Architectural or Historic Interest.

Finally, half a mile further down the Worfe is BROAD Bridge, carrying the Rabbit Run. This bridge consists of three arches, two of sixteen feet and the centre one of nineteen feet span, all of dressed red sandstone. The voussoirs of the facing rings are chamfered and there are prominent keystones. The parapets rise to a slight peak over the centre arch and there are six pilasters each side. An unsigned drawing of the bridge, dated 1800, shows the bridge as it appears today and with the piers and abutments founded on two layers of oak planking. I am sure it is Telford's work. This bridge was built to replace a single arch, brick bridge, which was in a very ruinous condition and had apparently been deteriorating for some time. In fact a temporary timber bridge had been erected alongside, some years previously, to provide a safer crossing for traffic. This had been washed away in the floods of 1795. The whole situation seems to be a good example of Telford's presence, in the County, being very much to the general good.

These then were the bridges built, in the County, during Telford's time as County Surveyor, up to the time of his death in 1834.

It is not the intention that this book should attempt to cover his activities as a builder of canals in the County, but some highway bridges over the canals are worth considering and this will be done in the next chapter.

IV

Some Canal Bridges and Minor Cast-Iron Bridges

The earliest canal system, built in the County, was sited in what is now the area of the New Town of Telford. This was developed for the purpose of moving coal, limestone and other products of the early days of the Industrial Revolution. So much recent development has taken place that most of the system and its highway bridges have been completely obliterated. However there is still some evidence of the oldest section, the Donnington Wood Canal and a few of its bridges, built by the second Earl Gower in the mid-1760s. Following the contours, and so obviating the need for locks, this started at Pave Lane, West of the Newport - Wolverhampton road, A41, and about a mile and a half South of Newport. All the canal has been out of use since the turn of the century and the land sold off for other uses. Many bridges were abandoned at the closure and though they have served no useful purpose for about eighty years, some still survive and there are traces of others. Under the circumstances it is not surprising that many have disappeared and the remainder are crumbling away. The best example is at PAVE LANE Bridge where the minor road from Pitchcroft crosses the filled-in line of the canal. This must have been a first rate piece of craftsmanship when it was built. It consists of a segmental brick arch, with a red sandstone pallet course and sandstone quoins at the ends of the abutments; the rest of the structure is of brick. A few years ago it was in very fair shape but its ultimate demolition must be only a matter of time.

A quarter of a mile South West of Pave Lane the bed of the canal has become the North drive to Lilleshall Hall, now a Physical Training Centre. LILLESHALL DRIVE Bridge, built as an occupation bridge, from one field to another, still fulfils that purpose, but over the drive. It is of similar construction to the one at Pave Lane and is spared the burden of carrying the traffic of a public highway. Its future must be threatened if the headroom it provides becomes a hazard to traffic using the drive.

Another branch of the canal runs Southwards from Pitchcroft and joins a third branch which served the old limestone quarry North of Lilleshall. At the junction of these two branches, Wildmoor Lane, a farm track running Eastwards out of Lilleshall, crosses the line of the canal over WILDMOOR LANE Bridge, also of similar construction to Pave Lane Bridge. When I visited it a few years ago it was becoming rather dilapidated and almost completely submerged in ivy and household refuse.

The Lilleshall Branch joins the Pave Lane Branch at HUGH'S Bridge which carries the West drive to Lilleshall Hall. The Lilleshall Branch ran at a lower level than the other and the junction was originally achieved by means of passing the lower level branch under the higher, in a tunnel. At the point of intersection a vertical shaft was sunk from one canal down to the other. Goods were transferred by means of a hoist powered by a donkey. In 1796 this laborious method of moving cargoes was eased by building an inclined plane connecting the two branches. A nearby terrace of houses bears a plate marked *Incline Cottages* though no evidence of the incline remains. Hugh's Bridge, carrying the drive, consists of cast-iron troughing and is believed to have been built in 1796.

The road from the South end of Lilleshall to Weston Heath crosses the line of the canal by LILLESHALL ABBEY Bridge, a similar cast-iron structure to Hugh's Bridge. This road was used as a tank transporter route during World War II and the cast-iron troughs of the bridge were filled with reinforced concrete, giving the old structure considerable strength without altering its character or appearance and, at the same time, enhancing its chances of survival. Visible from Lilleshall Abbey Bridge is a dry bridge in the middle of the Abbey Farmyard. ABBEY FARM Bridge is a segmental brick arch of rather plain appearance, without any stone quoins or pallet course. It must be very much in the way.

The extensive development of the Northern part of Telford New Town appears to have obliterated the remainder of this canal, with all its bridges. When I was walking the line of the canal, shortly before the modern development started, an elderly resident called to me that I must be looking for MARY ANNE PERRY'S Bridge. A lady, sitting on the doorstep of what must have been a canal-side cottage, before it was filled in, was happy to direct me. The line of the canal disappeared under a brick arch carrying the end of a new bungalow garden. This was all that was left of Mary Anne Perry's Bridge. The hilly nature of the terrain in the vicinity of this bridge, at Donnington Wood, suggests that the Donnington Wood inclined plane could have led up to it. This inclined plane made a canal through from Pave Lane and Lilleshall to Coalport possible.

Another branch leading off the canal at Donnington Wood ran *via* Trench and another incline which connected it to the Shrewsbury Canal. TEAGUES Bridge was a survivor on this length up to a few years ago. Its position is perpetuated by the name of the Bridge Inn at Teagues Bridge Road, between Donnington Wood and Trench, now a wide, modern thoroughfare but still Teagues Bridge Road. Though the canal was filled in the old bridge remained by the side of the road opposite the inn, a pretty structure of cast-iron with delicate wrought-iron parapet railings. It was removed to the Blists Hill museum where it is stored, awaiting a suitable site for its re-erection.

A canal authorized by Act of Parliament in 1791, was planned to run from Leominster, in Herefordshire to Stourport-on-Severn, passing through the Southern edge of the County. It was completed from Leominster to about ten miles short of Stourport. Its business must have been very limited and it produced little for its shareholders, finally selling out to the Shrewsbury and Hereford Railway Company in 1858. Much of the canal bed was then used to carry the now defunct branch line between Woofferton and Bewdley. One road bridge, over the old canal, survives on a length not taken over by the railway. Although the canal on either side was in Shropshire this bridge is, strictly speaking, just over the border, in Worcestershire. To find it, nearly two and a half miles after leaving the A49 at Woofferton, along the A456 road towards Tenbury, the bridge can be seen in the wood on the North side of the road, near the drive entrance to Easton Court. The remains of EASTON COURT Bridge consist of an eliptical stone arch, with spandrels and wing walls, all of finely dressed stone, more or less intact, together with the retaining wall which supported the tow path. The parapets have been demolished and the canal on either side filled in. There does not appear to be any roadway leading over the bridge which was doing duty as a hen house when I saw it. It must have been disused and not maintained for over a hundred and twenty years.

By 1944 the owners of the Shropshire Union Canal, the London, Midland and Scottish Railway Company, had suffered such heavy losses over the running of their canals that they promoted a Bill in Parliament which would result in the closure of all their canals passing through Shropshire with the exception of the Birmingham and Liverpool Canal. The Bill was passed and all the highway bridges over the canals to be closed became County Bridges and the County was compelled to bear the cost of their maintenance from then on. One of the conditions was that the County could assist with the closure of the canals, and at the same time ease the financial burden thrust upon it, by demolishing the bridges when this became expedient. Since the passing of the Act about thirty out of the hundred or so bridges taken over have been demolished.

This included four bridges on the Montgomery Branch from Welsh Frankton into Wales. With the revival of interest in this canal, however, largely due to the influence of the Prince of Wales Committee, with the financial support of Show Business Charities, demolition ceased, leaving seven bridges in the County intact. Volunteers, directed by the British Waterways Board, are working towards the complete restoration of this canal.

One of the canals now completely closed was the Shrewsbury Canal running to Donnington Wood and the same applied to the branch from that canal from Wappenshall Junction *via* Newport to join the Birmingham and Liverpool Canal at Norbury in Staffordshire. Three Telford bridges survive on the latter branch. NEWPORT Canal Bridge, carrying the old A41 road, which passed through the town, over the canal, is an eliptical arch of red sandstone with a "roving bridge" built out on the outside, clear of the highway for barge horses to cross from one side of the canal to the other. It was built in 1830 and the highway portion widened in stone faced brick some fifty years later. It is scheduled as an Ancient Monument.

Wappenshall Junction Canal Bridge built between 1830 and 1833. Most canal bridges cross squarely but this one crosses at a very sharp skew angle.

A typical, simple, straightforward canal bridge of the 1830s carries the road from Preston-upon-the-Weald Moors to Kynnersley over this branch. PRESTON Canal Bridge is a substantial structure mainly of red sandstone.

Perhaps the most important bridge over the branch is WAPPENSHALL JUNCTION Canal Bridge built between 1830 and 1833. Whereas the majority of canal bridges cross squarely this one crosses at a very sharp skew angle, involving fascinating shapes in the voussoirs of the elliptical stone arch. I have recently encountered an old book explaining methods of calculating and setting out the dressing of such stones; an intriguing aspect of nineteenth century engineering. This bridge is all curves, notably so when compared with the straight lines and angles of Newport Canal Bridge; it also has a roving bridge. Its demolition, by its owners, was just about to start when the County stepped in and took it over. It was completely restored, together with the surrounding landscape, in the 1970s and Scheduled as an Ancient Monument. It adjoins a brick warehouse, built over a barge dock with timber cranes for handling cargoes. The whole makes a pleasing little complex for people to visit and so a pedestrian right of way was established from the nearest point on the road. Unfortunately a drainage channel has been opened, cutting off the right of way, denying public access and reducing the chances of raising a public subscription to finance the proper preservation of the warehouse.

Happily the Ellesmere Canal, running from the Birmingham and Liverpool Canal at Hurlestone, in Cheshire, *via* Whitchurch and Ellesmere to Llangollen, was kept open. MAESTERMYN Canal Bridge had to be demolished in the interests of public safety and was replaced by a modern concrete bridge to full navigational standards by the County.

About two and a half miles South of Whitchurch, on the Ellesmere Canal is a timber lift bridge called BRICKWALLS Canal Bridge. An overhead gantry lifts the bridge with the assistance of a counterweight when a chain is pulled. As all the timber in the structure has to be replaced at fairly frequent intervals it is difficult to establish the date of its origin, though this would probably be soon after 1800, when the canal was built.

A couple of miles down the canal towards Llangollen the Prees Branch strikes out to the South and the first highway bridge, half a mile from the junction is STARK'S Canal Bridge, another timber lift bridge, superficially similar to Brickwalls Bridge. There is a difference however; whereas the latter bridge crosses the canal at right angles, Stark's Bridge crosses at a skew angle so that the shape of the whole structure is a parallelogram, including the lifting gear. This is straightforward enough while the bridge is down, but the complications of geometry set in when it is tilted up. Surely it must be about the only one of its kind in the world.

Canal bridges tend to follow a regular pattern of elliptical arches in brick or stone. However a variation crept in when the canal reached the vicinity of Chirk Bridge, over the River Ceiriog, where a minor road crosses it over CHIRK BANK Canal Bridge. Here for some reason Telford forsook the standard pattern and built a bridge whose abutments are of rubble masonry, while the

Stark's Canal Bridge is a rare example of a lift bridge which operates at a skew angle.

arch consists of about a dozen curved ribs of cast-iron. These supported an arched deck of timber baulks each of a length equal to the width of the bridge. These sleepers supported the filling material on which the roadway was laid. The parapets are of fair ashlar masonry and over the canal the lowest course is an ornamental arched lintel providing support for the parapet above it.

The cast-iron ribs were found to be theoretically incapable of carrying the weight of the filling material and road metalling, let alone any traffic. So, when the timbers had reached an appropriate state of deterioration, the road surfaces and filling material were removed and the sleepers replaced by permanent shuttering in the form of asbestos sheets, on which to cast a concrete slab. As the ribs were not capable of carrying wet concrete to the depth required for a reinforced concrete slab spanning the canal, a shallower slab was first cast on the asbestos shuttering. When this slab was strong enough to carry the rest of the wet concrete this was cast forming an extremely strong reinforced concrete deck, concealed in the old structure, whose appearance was not altered.

Sometimes canal builders had to provide structures outside the canal as accommodation works. A quarter of a mile East of where the canal passes under the A5 road between Chirk and Gobowen is BELMONT Canal Bridge. This is a run-of-the-mill brick canal bridge which carries the minor road from Henlle Hall Northwards to Glyn Morlais. Near this point the Morlas Brook passes under the canal and under the road. The original bridge carrying the road over the brook must have been demolished when the canal was built and so a new bridge had to be provided just North of the canal crossing. This is BROOKHOUSE Bridge which consists of three substantial stone arches with brick parapets. It seems likely that the brook bridge it replaced was a rather more modest structure by comparison. It was built in 1795.

It would perhaps be appropriate to look at some minor cast-iron bridges at this juncture.

In 1826 Lord Berwick financed the construction of a cast-iron arch bridge over the Cound Brook, about half a mile upstream of Cantlop Bridge, known then as Cliff Bridge but now better known as BORETON Bridge, after the hamlet a little way down the road. It was built with a cast-iron plate deck carried on five arch ribs of the same material. At some time the deck plates must have failed and a concrete deck was cast using corrugated iron sheets as shuttering; the latter are, of course, still there and exposed to view. This concrete was extended to enclose the parapets but leaving the vertical bars of the parapet railings uncovered. The impression given to the unsuspecting traveller is that here is a fairly modern concrete bridge. It is necessary to get underneath the bridge to see the cast-iron ribs, integral with the spandrel supports, which are clear of the concrete. The abutments are of brick and a plate at midspan gives the date 1826.

There appears to have been a tendency for some landowners, at this time, to set up what must have been a status symbol which took the form of a private underpass for their driveway to pass below the public highway. The North drive of Willey Hall passes under the Broseley - Barrow - Much Wenlock road, B4376, by means of WILLEY PARK Bridge, formed of cast-iron troughs with ornamental fascia ribs at the outside. The ornamentation of the fascia suggests Coalbrookdale casting as the pattern consists of a series of circles, diminishing in size towards midspan. A very small plate at midspan carries the date 1828. The last time I passed this bridge the fascias had been removed, I hope by the Estate staff who will replace them in due course. During World War II the cast-iron troughs were filled with reinforced concrete to increase the strength. The abutments, wing walls and parapets are all of brick, with flat stone coping on the parapets.

A very similar bridge carried the minor road from Acton Burnell to Kenley, over one of the Acton Burnell Hall driveways. ACTON BURNELL HALL Bridge carries the Smythe family crest, of a stag's head, together with the date 1829, cast at the centre of the fascia rib. In 1974 this narrow and rather hump-backed bridge had become insecure and a traffic hazard. With the ready permission of the owners the deck was removed and the driveway filled in. The brick parapets, including those of the wing walls, were rebuilt to a more suitable road width. One of the fascia ribs was fixed to the rebuilt brick parapet.

An extremely minor cast-iron bridge, CONDOVER HALL Bridge, provides an underpass from the main gardens of Condover Hall Blind School, under the Frodesley road, to the vegetable gardens. The deck is of cast-iron troughs and the roadside garden walls form the parapets. The date is believed to be about 1830.

The shortest route from the village of Rindleford to the village by Bromley, two miles North East of Bridgnorth, crosses the River Worfe by means of a ford, now impassable for vehicles. Pedestrians can cross by the old four span RINDLEFORD Footbridge. This may well have been a pack horse bridge with a timber deck. The four spans are supported by brick piers, capped with stone. Oak beams carry cast-iron deck plates and wrought-iron parapet railings. The beams have rotted through at the ends but have remained in position and the weight is carried by steel joists concealed behind the oak beams.

It was necessary for horse or pedestrian bridges to be provided to carry the River Severn tow-path over the various tributaries joining the main river. One such is MOR BROOK Bridge nearly three miles South of Bridgnorth. This is a cast-iron arch of thirty feet span. The plate at midspan states that it was cast by J. Onions of Broseley in 1824.

Four and a half miles further down the Severn is BORLE BROOK Bridge, a cast-iron arch of forty feet span, a mile below Highley. The downstream rib bears the inscription "Coalbrookdale Company 1828". The spandrel frames are formed of a series of iron rings, diminishing in size towards midspan.

V

Victoriana

[The North]

Having headed this chapter "Victoriana" I hope I may be forgiven for including some bridges, built during the short period between the termination of Thomas Telford's career as County Surveyor of Shropshire, by his death on 2nd September 1834, and the accession of Queen Victoria to the throne, on 20th June 1837. As Thomas Stanton was Telford's personal assistant, he appears to have vanished from the scene on the death of his chief. So Stanton's meticulous reports and drawings are succeeded by those of Edward Haycock, the new County Surveyor. We will, however, be looking at a few Stanton reports where these led to work being done after his departure from the scene.

Travelling Westwards from Shrewsbury, on the A5 and leaving that road at Wolfshead, for the B4396 road to Knockin and from there by the B4398, towards Llanymynech, brings us to PONT FADOC over the River Morda, about two and a half miles from Knockin. "Pont" or "Bont" frequently replaces "Bridge" as we approach the Welsh Border. Here Edward Haycock produced a design, dated 8th July 1836, for a new bridge to replace the "Ancient structure built of rubble stone". His drawing shows an elliptical masonry arch bridge with ornamental, chamfered voussoirs in the facing ring and of twenty feet span and five feet rise. The contract, to build the bridge for £566, was awarded to John Lloyd, Builder, from Llanymynech and Richard Milnes, Stonemason, of Oswestry and is dated 27th July 1836. The result is a well finished structure of ashlar masonry, the stone coming from Llanymynech Quarry.

About a mile North of Llanyblodwel, in the middle of an intensive quarrying area, is NANT MAWR Bridge, a stone arch of ten feet span and no great merit. However it is recorded that, in 1827, Stanton reported that the bridge, then standing, "was imperfectly constructed and must soon be rebuilt". He was apparently unable to get the work in hand before he retired, or perhaps the opinion of urgency was not shared and the problem waited for Edward Haycock who produced the design for the bridge as it now stands. It was built by John Cadman for £184, in 1844.

Pont Fadoc carrying the B4398 over the River Morda. 'Pont' or 'Bont' frequently replaces 'bridge' near the Welsh Border. (Photo. A. Blackwall).

Nearly three miles West of Oswestry, the Llansilin road, B4580, crosses the River Morda in a steep, rocky situation. The bridge involved is called LLAWNT Bridge and is a semicircular rubble arch of thirteen feet span, eighteen feet wide. In January 1836 Edward Haycock produced the design for the present bridge, which included very extensive wing walls to support the road above the steep banks of the river. The previous bridge to this one was built in 1750. The present one was built by Charles Lewis, Engineer and Isaac Porter, Builder from Oswestry, the contract being dated 4th April 1836. Stone, for the work, was obtained from a quarry on Carreg-y-beg, a mile away to the North.

For the next two bridges we must travel about six miles to the North of Oswestry and about sixty years forward in time. Both are of steel construction. PLAS THOMAS Bridge carries the minor road from Pentre Coed to Sodylt Bank, which is on the B5069. It is of fifteen feet span and is supported on rolled steel troughing with steel parapet railings; it was constructed in 1899. PONT LLYGODEN or MOUSE'S Bridge is intriguing only in its name. Its twenty-seven feet span is carried by two plate girders, two feet deep. The roadway is supported on rolled steel troughing resting on the bottom flanges of the girders, the parapet railings also being of steel. It was built in about 1900.

Three quarters of a mile down the A5 from Gobowen towards Whittington, lies Oak Mill crossroads and about half a mile along the lane leading to the North East is IRON MILLS Bridge over the River Perry. This very minor structure consists of a brick arch of seven feet span while the remainder of the structure is of rubble stone. There was a recommendation that the previous bridge was due for reconstruction, probably from Thomas Stanton, in 1812. However the matter was shelved until 1835 when there were exchanges of correspondence suggesting that it had become urgent. Thos. N. Parker Esq. of Sweeney Hall wrote to the Clerk of the Peace to say that he preferred single course stone parapets and had been responsible for their use on a number of bridges in the vicinity. Some may still be seen about. Mr. Lovett of Fernhill wrote to say that he would be prepared to pay for the bed of the river to be lowered by three feet in the vicinity of the bridge. The contract to build the new bridge was awarded to Robert Roberts, Gas Proprietor, in 1836. The specification called for a seven feet span arch bridge with an inverted arch in the bed of the river. It might be wondered if the latter provision was to prevent Mr. Lovett from carrying out the river deepening which would be to improve the drainage of his land, possibly at the expense of others. Foundations were to be thirteen feet below road level. It would appear that Mr. Parker's choice of parapets was not used. Edward Haycock later reported some scour to the foundations but that this would be checked by tipping in stone from Sweeney Mountain.

The road from Stanwardine-in-the-Fields to Wykey, a village a couple of miles North of Ruyton-XI-Towns, crosses the River Perry by JUBILEE Bridge, so called because it was built in 1887, the fiftieth year of Queen Victoria's reign. This is a thirty feet span bridge, carried on four steel beams, each thirteen inches deep and six inches across the flanges. The deck is of steel plates. The material has all the characteristics of steel but the date of construction puts it in the era of transition from wrought iron to steel, so it could be the former.

Half a mile out of Loppington, along the B4397 road towards Wem is SPENDFORD or SPENFORD Bridge, a dressed sandstone bridge supported by a three ring brick arch of fifteen feet span, over the River Roden. In 1829 there was a structure here consisting of four three feet wide openings each covered by a sandstone slab. The whole thing was in a parlous condition and, at the time, repairs were proposed. However Major Thomas Dicken of Loppington House, which is immediately upstream of the bridge, complained that it obstructed the flow of the river, causing flooding on his land. He demanded that the invert or bed under the bridge should be lowered. Thomas Stanton pointed out in a letter of 31st December 1830 that this would call for a new bridge, costing £200 instead of repairs for £40. Joseph Loxton, the Clerk of the Peace, placed the information before the Magistrates who decided that repairs should be carried out. So the old bridge remained until 20th September 1861 when Edward Haycock recommended that a fifteen feet span brick arch bridge be built on the existing abutments and the slabs and intermediate piers removed. The difficulty over the flow of the river would be alleviated by means of an inverted arch in the bed. He estimated that this could be done for £70 or £80. A contract to carry out the work was awarded to John Treasure on 19th August 1862.

The River Roden flows through the hamlet of Aston, a mile East of Wem, under ASTON Bridge, a segmental arch bridge of ashlar masonry, eighteen feet in span. In 1826 there was a ford for vehicles, with a narrow bridge for pedestrians and horses, built of timber on stone piers, a type sometimes referred to as a "Pack and Prime" bridge. At that time Thomas Stanton noted the condition of the old structure and considered that it should be replaced by a vehicular bridge of thirty-three feet span which he estimated would cost £600. This the Magistrates would not accept and the pack and prime bridge had to continue in use until 1840 when Edward Haycock decided the replacement was due but that a span of eighteen feet with a rise of three feet would be sufficient. Edward and William Lewis estimated that they could build this for £240 and were awarded the contract to do so on 5th February 1841. It is remarkable how, then as now, politicial or financial pressures compelled construction work to be undertaken at an unsuitable season of the year. The troubles experienced in the construction of the next bridge, due to this cause, will perhaps serve as an example.

In 1881 the bridge at Paper Mill Bank which carried what is now a private road across Harcourt Park, from Besford towards Hopton and Hodnet, over the Roden, was in trouble. The bridge, at that time, was of two arches totalling thirty-six feet and the road was described as the Preston Brockhurst to Hodnet and Market Drayton Main Road. PAPER MILL Bridge was therefore accepted as a County responsiblity and it is included in the 1901 County Bridge List. At

Stanton River Bridge built in 1873. The River Roden now runs under the reconstructed Mill Bridge half a mile away so the river bed here is dry except at flood time.

the time that the old bridge became unsafe the County Surveyor, Thomas Groves prepared the design for a twenty feet span sandstone arch bridge. The contractors appointed to build the bridge were Messrs. John Done and Son, of Hadnall, the contract being dated 8th September 1881. Demolition of the old bridge and excavation for foundations began some time after this date and, perhaps due to a start at the outset of winter, the operation was soon in trouble, with the excavation continually flooded. After struggling for some time John Done asked to be released from the contract. Whether he was released and if so who completed the work, hopefully in the spring, is not recorded. The bridge, as it stands today, was built at that time to Thomas Groves' design.

Local residents apparently made further trouble for the unfortunate Mr. Done whom, they claimed, they had seen removing timber which they presumed to be the property of the County, from the site. Such timber however would almost certainly have been the property of the contractor as the bridge was being built of stone. The outcome of this dispute is unfortunately not recorded either.

The road from Stanton-upon-Hine Heath to Moreton Corbett has to cross what was once the supply to Stanton Mill, a crossing we have already dealt with, and then the River Roden itself. Of this latter crossing it was reported to the Magistrates, on 14th April 1872, that STANTON RIVER Bridge was in a ruinous condition and must be replaced. As a result of this a specification was drawn up, dated 29th July 1873, calling for a segmental stone arch bridge of twenty-four feet span and providing a road width of eleven feet. A contract was entered into with William Jones of Clive, on 20th September 1873, to build the new bridge for £245. As the main flow of the river now runs under the reconstructed Mill Bridge the Stanton River Bridge is over a dry bed except at flood time.

Following the Roden downstream from Stanton brings us to the village of Shawbury, at the East end of which is SHAWBURY Bridge carrying the Shawbury - Hodnet road, A53. This is an impressive structure of three arches, two of fourteen feet and the centre span of sixteen feet. The whole is finely constructed of red and white sandstone ashlar and block in course masonry. The facing rings are embellished with archivolts and decorated keystones. Its width, as built, was twelve feet and was widened to forty-five feet in 1936. The arches were extended in reinforced concrete, faced with new stone to match the original. The parapet on the widened side was re-used complete. None of the documents referring to this bridge give any clue to the date of its construction. Thomas Stanton reported on the dilapidations of its predecessors in 1823 and there are several references to the state of the road. However Edward Haycock commented on the work required to put the piers and abutments into good order on 21st February 1856. It is then perhaps reasonable to assume that the present bridge was built after that date, possibly shortly after, as the running down of the old bridge must have been fairly advanced by that time. The stonework of the present bridge does not suggest that it could have been subject to Haycock's comments in 1856.

The next bridge encountered by following the Roden downstream is in the hamlet of Poynton Green, about a mile and a half below Shawbury. POYNTON

Bridge is a neat structure with a semicircular arch of fifteen feet six inches span, carrying a road eleven feet wide. Unfortunately the documents purporting to refer to the history of this bridge in fact refer to a timber footbridge which presumably preceded it.

A little over three miles below Poynton Bridge brings us to Rodington where the river flows under the East end of the village. Here, RODINGTON Bridge is a lattice through girder bridge, of wrought iron and of forty feet span. (Perhaps we could remind ourselves, at this point, that a through girder bridge is one whose deck is at the level of the bottom boom of the main girders and so the roadway runs through, between them). Rodington Bridge was built by the Wellington Union Rural Sanitary Authority, to the design of John Breeze, the Surveyor to the Authority, for £857 in 1884. The abutments are of brick and the specification calls for bearing stones from Grinshill Quarry to support the girders on the brickwork. The girders are of normal lattice construction, forty-four feet long and five feet deep, the deck being originally of buckle plates supported on cross beams. The wrought ironwork was all fabricated by the Coalbrookdale Company at their Horsehay Works, for £336. In 1960 the deck was strengthened in the form of a reinforced concrete slab.

Before we go any further we must look at a couple of outlying bridges which might otherwise be missed. Three and a half miles North West of Market Drayton lies Shavington Park with its Hall at the centre. The minor road from Adderley to Wilkesley runs through the North East corner of the Park, crossing the River Duckow in the process. There are two bridges, called SHAVINGTON Bridges, built by the estate in Victorian times and widened by the County by extending the arches in reinforced concrete and re-using the external masonry, in 1940. These are two fine, if modest, structures of ashlar masonry, one consisting of two spans of fourteen feet and the other, one span of the same size.

[The West]

To look at the Victorian bridges to the West of Shrewsbury we will start out along the old Bishops Castle Turnpike, now usually referred to as the Longden Road, past the hamlet of Nobold and over Red Hill railway bridge. Before the road reaches Hookagate there is a lane leading off to the left and crossing the Rea Brook. The bridge carrying the lane across the brook is quite impressive, a lofty five ring brick arch, of about twenty feet span, on tall red sandstone abutments. The spandrels and wing walls are also of rock-faced sandstone blocks, while what remains of the parapets is of brick with stone coping. The whole gives the impression of railway engineering of the 1860s. It carried a colliery railway servicing pits in the Pulley - Hookagate area. I have called it, for the sake of convenience, RED HILL COLLIERY Bridge.

Next we will move up the Rea Brook to Great Hanwood, on the A488, modern route to Bishops Castle. HANWOOD Bridge carries this road over the brook. In 1837 the road was part of the Shrewsbury - Minsterley Turnpike and a report was prepared for the Trustees by a Mr. Snook, pointing out the need for a new bridge. A broadsheet was issued saying "As a new bridge is most desirable the

Trustees of the Ministerley Road have been requested to make Application to the Nobility and Gentry, possessed of Landed Property, concerned with Mines etc. or otherwise interested in this Line of Road, for their subscriptions towards rebuilding the Bridge". Tenders had been invited for the work, the lowest being that from Thomas Carline for £745. The broadsheet appeal raised £150. In spite of this shortfall the contract was given to Carline who, in 1838, built first a temporary timber bridge for the public to use while the new bridge was under construction. This was built as an elliptical arch of forty feet span, of dressed Grinshill stone. The parapets were formed of a single course of dressed stone, as proposed by Mr. Thomas Parker of Sweeney Hall for Iron Mills Bridge. Hanwood Bridge remains as it was built except for the addition of a steel footbridge.

A mile and a half from Great Hanwood, along the A488 road towards Minsterley, is a road junction called Lea Cross. From here the minor road, leading Northwards towards Nox and Yockleton crosses the Rea Brook by LEA Bridge. In 1884 the road crossed the brook by means of a ford, with a narrow bridge for pedestrians and horses. J. H. Hoult, District Surveyor to the Condover Highways Board, prepared the necessary documents for the construction of a vehicular bridge. This was planned to be a lattice through girder bridge of thirty-six feet span, eighteen feet six inches wide. For the foundations the specification required "Five parts of broken stone or washed gravel to one part of Portland Cement. External water to be kept away (from the concrete so formed) for six hours and masonry not to be built on it for eight hours". This is certainly an early reference to the structural use of Portland Cement concrete in the County. Stone for the "Shoddy-faced masonry" with ashlar quoins was to come from Cardeston Quarry. The main contractor for the construction was a Mr. Brown, the ironwork being fabricated by Carter Ford and Company. The final cost was £460 against Mr. Hoult's estimate of £668. The intention was that the construction should be to the satisfaction of the County Surveyor, Thomas Groves, so that the bridge would be taken over by the County. By 1901 it was included in the County Bridge List.

The B4386 road, through Nox and Yockleton, crosses the Nox Brook, a tributary of the Rea Brook, twice. Lynches Bridge near Nox has been recently replaced by a reinforced concrete structure. YOCKLETON Bridge, towards the West end of the village, was designed by Edward Haycock. The specification was for the twelve feet span arch to be of five rings of bricks, faced with Grinshill Stone. The foundations, abutments, spandrels and wing walls were to be of Cardeston Stone. The ornamental string course and newels were to be of Grinshill Stone. The contract for construction, dated 18th July 1853, was awarded to John Thomas of Church Stoke, for a price of £222. The completion date was set as Christmas Day 1853.

Eleven miles Westwards down the B4386 from Yockleton the road crosses the River Camlad by HOCKLETON Bridge. There was a timber bridge here in 1832 which Thomas Stanton reported to be in poor condition at that time. He prepared a design for a segmental stone arch bridge of twenty-five feet span and ten feet rise, the facing ring to consist of ornamental voussoirs with stepped extrados. His estimate was for £820. However before this could be put in hand Telford's death and Stanton's retirement intervened. In 1835 Edward Haycock, the new County Surveyor, prepared the design for an elliptical arch bridge of the same span as Stanton's. The contract for construction, dated 30th June 1835, was awarded to Joseph Stant of Shrewsbury, for £972. John and Thomas Carline's tender was unsuccessful. The work was well executed and a fine and elegant structure is the surviving evidence.

If we next follow the B4386 to Chirbury and there turn Northwards towards Welshpool, on the A490, we would cross the Camlad again by SHIREGROVE Bridge, just short of the Welsh border which does not now follow the river at this point. The bridge is a thirty feet span lattice through girder bridge on stone abutments. It was built during 1881-82 by Price and Sons for £400, the ironwork being fabricated by the Coalbrookdale Company, at their Horsehay Works. In 1950 the deck was strengthened in reinforced concrete.

Presumably by 1882 Shiregrove Bridge had been accepted by the County. In earlier days the County administration fought shy of it. In 1795 the local residents had been compelled, by the County Court, to provide a new stone bridge, the earlier timber structure being no longer safe. Attention was called to this by Col. Davies of Marrington Hall in a letter of 31st March 1841. By that time it was claimed locally that the road was the Welshpool - Bishops Castle main road, but the County denied liability, saying that the road had been diverted to suit local convenience. Comparing old maps suggests that the diversion only amounted to moving the site of the bridge a few yards upstream. In any case the road had been a Turnpike since 1801.

Three quarters of a mile East of Chirbury the minor road to Priest Weston crosses the River Camlad over WHITTREY Bridge. In 1873 Aaron Hamer, Surveyor to the Bishops Castle Highways Board, prepared the design for a segmental brick arch of four rings, twenty-four feet in span, supporting a bridge the remainder of which was to be of rubble masonry from Whittrey Quarry. This appears to be the bridge which stands today. Earlier, in 1829, there was a ford with a pack and prime bridge which was the subject of a meeting at the Cross Inn, Chirbury on 10th October of that year. It was agreed that a carriage bridge should be built, for which £120 had been collected by local subscription. The responsibility for action in the matter appears to have been taken by the Trustees of the Chirbury - Church Stoke Turnpike. They forwarded a drawing and specification, which they had prepared, to Joseph Loxton, the Clerk of the Peace, with the request that the County Surveyor should superintend the construction. If this was done in 1830 the bridge can have stood for only forty-three years until Aaron Hamer's bridge replaced it. The answer is probably a massive flood on the Camlad in 1829.

[The South East]

Our route is now from Shrewsbury towards Ironbridge, along the B4380. Four miles West of Ironbridge is the village of Leighton, famed as the birthplace of the Shropshire novelist Mary Webb. Here the road is carried over a brook which runs into the River Severn. In 1775 Edward Owen of Eaton Constantine built a stone bridge for the purpose. There is an account for the purchase of two quarts of ale for men repairing this structure in 1852 and for three shillings paid to three women, who worked in the coal pits, for bringing three loads of stone for the work. However, by 1869 Thomas Groves, the County Surveyor, decided that a new bridge was due and prepared the design for the present LEIGHTON Bridge. This shows a nine feet span semicircular arch bridge of three brick rings, the rest of the structure also being of brick. The specification lays down that Jackfield or Broseley bricks were to be used. Details of placing concrete in the foundations are set out ". . . composed of clean washed gravel and consisting of three parts of gravel to one of Lump Steeraway or Wenlock Lime; broken up before being mixed and thrown from a stage ten feet above the deposit; the whole being thoroughly mixed and turned over before being used". The completion date was to be 1st September 1869 and the contractors were Henry Watkin and William Price of Shrewsbury. Their quotation was for £335. The resulting bridge is of neat design, well executed, the pilasters and newels being capped with Grinshill Stone. The slight widening on the downstream side is supported on a steel beam.

A mile South of Leighton, on the other side of the River Severn, the minor road from Cressage to Much Wenlock, *via* Sheinton, crosses the Harley Brook over SHEINTON Bridge, a quarter of a mile West of the village. This is a fairly narrow three arch brick bridge, the centre span being of sixteen feet and the other two of eleven feet. Abutments and piers however are of stone, suggesting that an earlier stone bridge failed but its abutments and piers were sound enough to support a new brick superstructure. Unfortunately no dates or other information about the construction of the bridge survive. It is known, however, that when the opening of the Iron Bridge diverted Bridgnorth-bound traffic from the stiff climb up Harley Hill, the Wenlock Turnpike Trustees opened up this Sheinton road as a second alternative to that *via* the Iron Bridge. The route, to start with, must have relied on the old stone bridge, the brick one following in due course. The first written evidence of it is a report on its condition by Edward Haycock in 1838. About fifty years ago a load restriction was applied to the bridge resulting in the setting up of a sign similar to that at Aston Park Bridge, in Chapter 3. This sign or one like it, from Clun Bridge, is now in the National Motor Museum at Beaulieu, in Hampshire.

The next bridge, up the Harley Brook from Sheinton, is HARLEY Bridge. This is at the South end of the village of Harley and carries the Shrewsbury - Much Wenlock road, A458. Harley is now happily relieved of the main road traffic by the by-pass on its East side. In connection with the construction of the by-pass, in the 1960s, Harley Bridge was widened on both sides of the road. The arch was extended in reinforced concrete and the new spandrels, wing walls and parapets are of brick. So to find the original bridge we must look underneath. In 1843 the Trustees of the Turnpike petitioned the County Magistrates for £300 towards the cost of a new bridge, the remainder to be raised by local subscription. Originally they proposed an extensive road diversion, making the total cost £600, but this was apparently abandoned. A drawing was submitted by a designer, whose name is lost, showing a very pleasing cast-iron bridge, for the situation, but it was evidently not used. The drawing survives. Edward Haycock designed a bridge based on a semicircular arch of three brick rings and of sixteen feet span. Spandrels, wing walls and abutments were to be of rubble masonry, the parapets being of brick with string course and coping of tooled Grinshill Stone. His design, dated 1843, represents the bridge now immured in the centre of the present structure.

The village of Badger lies five miles North East of Bridgnorth, not far from the Staffordshire boundary. Badger Hall, surrounded by its Park, is near the church. A woodland walk was laid out, from the Hall, Southwards across the Park, to the picturesque Badger Dingle. This walk crosses the road from Badger to Badger Heath over BADGER Bridge. It would perhaps be more explicit to say that the public road passes through a brick tunnel, forty feet long, under the walk. A sign over the ends of the tunnel declares that the headroom is eight feet nine inches which must cause some inconvenience with loads of hay. The whole structure is well finished in brick with stone coping on the parapets which flank the walk. The abutments continue in both directions along the road as retaining walls. Since its construction the top of the bridge has given hospitality to a large number of self-sown conifers, of which many are now full grown and, if they are not removed, it will only be a matter of time before their roots destroy their host.

Patshull Hall is situated over the boundary, in Staffordshire, two and a half miles North East of Badger. On the edge of the grounds of the Hall is a small bridge over the North end of the Long Pond. It carries the last few yards of a public road and is maintained by the County by arrangement with the County of Staffordshire because of convenience of access. This is WILDECOTE Bridge and I include it as an example of a public highway bridge, built by the owners of a private park for the public good, but at the same time featuring in the landscaping of the park. The bridge consists of a brick arch of modest span, faced on the side seen from the Hall, with fine ashlar masonry. The arch is faced with ornamental voussoirs, a prominent keystone and moulded archivolt. With its elegant balustrade parapet of lathe-turned stone it must have looked well from the Hall, before the trees grew up to obscure the view. To prove my point we look at the other side of the bridge, not visible from the Hall and find it finished in common brick, with the exception of the parapet.

We now move to Morville, on the A458 road, three miles West of Bridgnorth and follow the B4368 road from there towards Craven Arms. Our purpose is to look at three stone bridges, built by the Turnpike Trust responsible for the "New Turnpike Road from Morville to Shipton" in 1841. First, on the outskirts of Morville the Mor Brook is crossed by ASH Bridge, a masonry arch of seventeen feet span, now a Listed Structure of Architectural or Historic Interest. It is supported by stone buttresses to prevent the spandrels and facing ring from falling outwards. The next bridge, of this trio of stone bridges, we find is MONK HOPTON Bridge, of ten feet span, over the Beaconhill Brook. Finally we cross the River Corve over SHIPTON Bridge, into the village. This is a well built rubble masonry structure of sixteen feet span and, like the previous two bridges it retains its original width of nineteen feet. The parapets are of three courses of

Wildecote Bridge. This is the side seen from the hall and is faced with fine ashlar masonry.

Still the same bridge but from the other side. Finished only in common brick with the exception of the ornate ballustrade.

dressed stone, the top course being dressed to form a bull-nosed coping to match the string course. The finish of the parapets, being rather better than the rest of the stonework, suggests that they may be of a later date. A letter from Edward Haycock to the Clerk of the Peace, dated 18th December 1841, refers to three bridges, "built recently, on the new road from Morville to Shipton, which may be accepted as County Bridges".

Five miles down the B4368, from Shipton towards Craven Arms is the village of Diddlebury where this main road crosses a minor tributary of the Corve, by BACHE MILL Bridge, a stone arch of eight feet span, with a stone plaque saying that it was "Erected by I. Overton 1850".

The Bridgnorth - Ludlow road, B4364, crosses the Winterburn Brook nearly five miles from Bridgnorth and not far from Faintree Hall. Here the road once fell sharply down to the brook, negotiated a little hump-backed bridge and then faced the steep climb up the other side of the valley. In 1847 Edward Haycock decided to improve this situation by raising the road on an embankment across the valley and at the same time enclosing the brook in the stone-arched FAINTREE TUNNEL, of nine feet span, six feet headroom and a hundred and fifty-seven feet long. The work of constructing the (cut and cover) tunnel was carried out by George Snook of Wellington for £250. As a waterproofing membrane he covered the extrados of the tunnel arch with puddled clay. The embankment was built up by the Bridgnorth - Cleobury North Turnpike Trustees.

Six miles South East of Faintree Tunnel the road from the Bridgnorth - Cleobury Mortimer road B4363, North of Kinlet, to the mining village of Highley, crosses the Borle Brook just East of the hamlet of Netherton. The bridge over the brook is known as BORLE MILL Bridge. No details, of any kind, can be found of the history of this bridge. It is however listed as a Structure of Architectural or Historic Interest. It is a neat structure of coursed or snecked rubble, including the arch which is almost semicircular and of twenty-four feet span. There is a string course and above it the parapets and coping are of larger dressed stones. The road over the bridge is no longer the main access to Highley. This follows the B4555, by-passing Borle Mill Bridge and crossing the brook by the modern reinforced concrete OUTRACK Bridge and the now disused colliery railway by a steel girder bridge, both built in the 1930s.

In Chapter 1 we looked at Old Roman Bridge, between Stottesdon and Prescott, over the River Rea and noted that due to this bridge being referred to as "Bridge North of Prescott Mill" there may be some confusion with PRESCOTT MILL Bridge which we will now consider. This bridge is about a quarter of a mile downstream from Old Roman Bridge and carries the Oreton - Prescott - Bagginswood minor road over the Rea. It is built of coursed rubble masonry, the span being twenty-eight feet. That is really all that I can say about it as no records of its history appear to exist. Its construction is judged to have taken place at some time in the Victorian era.

The Ludlow - Cloebury Mortimer - Bewdley road, A4117, crosses the Mill Brook, over HOPTON WAFERS Bridge, a sixteen feet span stone arch, two miles East of Cleobury Mortimer. A quarter of a mile upstream of Hopton

Wafers Bridge a minor road crosses the brook by HOPTON COURT Bridge. This is a more impressive structure, a four brick ring arch of eighteen feet span on abutments which rise fifteen feet above the bed of the brook. The parapets and roadway appear to have been raised so that the top of the parapet at midspan is now about thirty feet above the brook. It was probably built at the expense of the owner of Hopton Court and no public record exists of its construction.

While we are in the Cleobury Mortimer area we may remember LOWER FORGE Footbridge, over the River Rea about a mile below the town. This bridge, which has just been replaced by a modern structure, was, at sixty feet span an interesting example of Victorian engineering, the width being only a yard in spite of the considerable span and a system of diagonal sway-braces was incorporated, tensioned with turnbuckles, concealed under the wooden deck. The main bearers were steel beams, ten inches deep, stiffened below by outriggers of "T" section members. The path from the Cleobury Mortimer - Bayton road is a bridle path and leaves the road through a farm-yard. Though the old footbridge is no longer to be seen the remains of the forge together with a cattle ford, cut into the bed of the steeply falling river, is quite an interesting little complex.

Continuing Southwards down the same road we reach the River Rea, which is the boundary with the County of Hereford and Worcester at HAUGHTONSPOLE Bridge. This is an elliptical arch bridge of thirty feet span, consisting of three brick rings, high above the river on tall brick abutments, the spandrels and wing walls being of rubble. At the top of each abutment is a brick-lined culvert or tunnel whose purpose must be to lighten the overall weight. The roadway is on a comparatively recent concrete deck projecting over the sides of the bridge to provide extra width. There are further concrete projections to carry the outrigged stays to the steel parapet handrail stancheons. By agreement Hereford and Worcester look after this bridge.

Three miles East of Cleobury Mortimer is a small bridge carrying the minor road, from Lem Hill, on the A4117, to Bradley, on the B4363, passing through the Western fringe of the Wyre Forest. This is FURNACE MILL Bridge. Over the ten feet span arch the date stone is inscribed "T.B. 1871". The water power here was probably employed driving a blower for the furnace and there may be traces of the industrial complex of which it was a part.

[The South and West]

Finally, for this Chapter, we leave Shrewsbury and this time, to the South, along the A49 but after Bayston Hill we leave the trunk road to turn left into Condover. CONDOVER NEW Bridge, carrying the Frodesley road over the Cound Brook, is a plate girder bridge of thirty-six feet span, the main girders being four feet deep. The deck is of buckle plates on transverse beams. In 1883 the Condover Highways Board entered into a contract with Mr. Williams, Stonemason, and the Dyne Steel Company to build the bridge for £603, of which £200 was a grant from the County. Back in 1826 Thomas Stanton had carried out repairs to the earlier stone bridge and a pack and prime bridge was mentioned before that. The waterway provided by the stone bridge was probably inadequate as Edward Haycock was putting forward proposals for a relief culvert in 1846.

A mile North of Dorrington the A49 is crossed by a minor road from Stapleton to Great Ryton. A few yards from the trunk road, towards Great Ryton is GONSAL Bridge which is a lattice through girder bridge of thirty feet span, on brick abutments over the Cound Brook. The deck is of cross beams and buckle plates. There is no record of its construction which probably took place in the 1880s. I have a happy memory of work on this bridge about thirty years ago. Repairs involving welding were being carried out by a welder renowned for his extensive vocabulary. He inadvertently fumbled his hammer which fell into the brook, with a splash. After waiting for his comments, which however did not materialize, I was fascinated to watch him pull a large horseshoe magnet out of his tool bag, attached to a line, which he quickly lowered into the water and, after casting around for a moment, fished out the hammer and hauled it up, in ominous silence and continued work.

We now move across to the old Bishops Castle Turnpike and continue Southwards along it for six miles after passing Castle Pulverbatch. That will take us to (GRAVENOR) UPPER MILL Bridge over the River East Onny. There is a specification, dated 1852, for a stone arch bridge here. If it was built then it can have lasted for only twenty-seven years, as Thomas Groves, County Surveyor, reported it to be in poor condition and due for replacement in 1879. Following this report it was replaced by the present lattice through girder, skew bridge of twenty-two feet span in 1880-81. The lattice girders and deck plates were fabricated by the Coalbrookdale Company. In 1978 a reinforced concrete slab, spanning the river, was cast using the iron deck as permanent shuttering. The lattice girders remain as if they were supporting the bridge but are, in fact, now just parapets.

A mile down the road towards Bishops Castle is WALKMILL Bridge, over the River East Onny, near Wentnor. We have already met a bridge of this name at Market Drayton. This one however is a Listed Structure of Architectural or Historic Interest, not apparently so much on its own merit, but due to its involvement with the cottage and gardens grouped around it. A drawing, dated 1850 and purporting to refer to the construction of this bridge survives, showing rubble construction and comprising two elliptical arches of twelve feet span each, with plain dressed voussoirs in the facing rings. The bridge as it stands, however, consists of two segmental arches, the remaining details being according to the drawing. The downstream parapet wall has been replaced by cast-iron railings to assist with visibility on a dangerous corner.

Half a mile further along the road is a turning off to left, to Whitcot where the East Onny is spanned by WHITCOT Bridge. Here the tracing of a drawing exists, dated 10th August 1882, showing a stone arch of twenty-feet span. There is also an estimate by Aaron Hamer, Surveyor to the Bishops Castle Highways Board for £230. This was sent to the Clerk of the Peace for approval but for some reason got no further.

74

Walkmill Bridge. The downstream parapet has been replaced by cast-iron railings to aid visibility on a dangerous corner.

In 1888 the Local Government Act authorized the formation of County Councils, including that for Shropshire. The County Council then in 1898 agreed to pay one third of the £450 required to build a bridge, of twenty two feet span, consisting of rolled steel troughing and steel parapet handrails, at Whitcot. By this time the next Local Government Act of 1894 had resulted in the formation of the Clun Rural District Council and this authority produced another third of the cost. The remainder having been raised by local subscription, the bridge was completed in 1898.

The River East Onny joins the West Onny a little over a mile downstream from Whitcot. The River Onny proper then flows Eastward under EATON Bridge which carries the minor road from Wentnor and Myndtown to join the Lydham - Wistanstow road, A489, at Eaton. The bridge is of rubble masonry and consists of two segmental arches of sixteen feet span each. It is a nicely proportioned bridge, generally pleasing and is Listed as a Structure of Architectural or Historic Interest. Prior to 1842 there was a ford and a horsebridge of two timber spans, in the form of king post trusses, on stone piers. It provided a crossing about six feet wide. In that year the County Surveyor, Edward Haycock produced the design for the present stone bridge which was built by Thomas Simons for £300. Simons at first expressed a preference for building a timber bridge, of vehicular width, which he offered to do for £170.

The road joining the hamlet of Little Brampton to the village of Clunbury, about four miles West of Craven Arms, crosses the River Kemp by LITTLE

BRAMPTON Bridge, shortly before its confluence with the River Clun. In 1843 Edward Haycock designed a stone arch bridge, the arch being of twenty feet span and six feet six inches rise, of dressed stone. The rest of the structure is shown in his drawing as being of snecked rubble but with ashlar quoins to the abutments. Matthew Stead, the younger, contracted on 9th September 1843 to build the bridge for £222, which survives as a fair monument to his workmanship. The only recent modification is the underpinning of the abutments, with concrete, to combat scour.

Continuing Southwards from Little Brampton the same road then crosses the River Clun by CLUNBURY Bridge. Edward Haycock was also responsible for this bridge. His drawing shows a thirty feet span elliptical arch bridge with ornamental voussoirs in the facing rings. The parapets and string course are flat, without any hint of camber. Perhaps Haycock decided that a flat bridge complemented its elliptical arch while a cambered bridge set off a segmental arch. It is worth thinking about and I agree until the next time I see a brick canal bridge with its elliptical arch perfectly balanced by the flowing curves of its cambered parapets. For Clunbury Bridge the contract, dated 4th April 1837, also went to Matthew Stead, who had offered a quotation of £400. Other tenders were received but were generally around £600. For the construction the stone came from the Earl of Powys' Clunbury Hill Quarry. The site of the bridge is a little upstream of the earlier, timber structure which Thomas Stanton had repaired in 1817. As the new bridge was on a fresh site, land acquisition became involved. Difficulties arose with the landlady of the adjoining inn, who objected to losing a corner of her property for £1. The Clerk of the Peace asked the Magistrates to invoke their powers of compulsory purchase, under the Bridge Acts. It would be interesting to know how the matter was settled.

Half a mile upstream from Clunbury the Purslow - Hopton Heath road, B4385, crosses the River Clun over PURSLOW CLUN Bridge. A drawing dated 1872 shows a single arch bridge, twenty-six feet in span, of four rings of Broseley bricks. The parapets, spandrels and wing walls are of snecked rubble which was to be got from Radnor Quarry, while infill rubble was to come from Twitchen. Dressed stone for arch skewbacks, string course and coping is described as "of Long Low Stone". The wing walls on both sides of the river are shown as pierced by four feet flood openings. The bridge was built according to the drawing except that it only has one flood opening. The coping of the parapet rises pleasingly to a peak at midspan and the general impression is one of massive construction.

A mile down the River Clun from Clunbury, at Aston-on-Clun the river is spanned by BEAMBRIDGE, the second bridge with this name we have encountered. This is the site of an old bridge, now occupied by a steel beam bridge, built by the Clun Rural District Council in 1908. In 1794, after a disastrous flood which had swept away the bridge then standing here, funds were raised from the people of Aston-on-Clun and a timber decked horsebridge was built by "Harley, a carpenter of Hopton Castle". By 1813 this structure must have been in some trouble as enquiries were being made as to the responsibility for its replacement. In 1826 the people of the village were found guilty of the neglect of the bridge, by a Grand Jury and the village constables levied a rate of £10 from them, an interesting insight into police responsiblities at that time. After that repair the next mention of the bridge was in 1849 when it was described as an "Ancient wooden structure" and attempts were made to persuade the County to take it over, after suitable repairs and overhaul. As it was evidently a Rural District Council responsibility in 1908 it would seem that these were unsuccessful.

We must now move Eastwards, through Craven Arms, onto the B4368 road from there towards Morville. On leaving Craven Arms the road crosses the River Onny at CLUNSFORD Bridge. Here in 1834, as we have seen, Thomas Stanton supervised the construction of a masonry bridge. By 1886 this structure must have been in trouble and Thomas Groves, the County Surveyor, decided that a single span lattice through girder bridge should replace it. This was approved and the contract for the stonework in the abutments and wing walls was awarded to Thomas Miller, stonemason of Craven Arms. Tenders were received, for the wrought ironwork in the lattice girders and deck, from Thomas Woodall's Windmill Works at Dudley and from the Coalbrookdale Company. The latter company were successful and contracted to complete the ironwork for £370. The fifty-four feet span bridge is still in use and in recent years a steel footbridge was added to the upstream side.

Two and a half miles South of Craven Arms the A49 crosses the River Onny over another wrought iron girder bridge at Onibury. The lattice girders supporting ONIBURY Bridge are beneath the deck, instead of on either side of it, and have cambered lower flanges, giving a pleasing soffit line to the structure. It is of three spans, the centre span being of fifty-five feet and the two side spans thirty feet each. The two piers consist of cast-iron trestles on stone plinths. Thomas Groves had prepared the design for the bridge in 1886 and contracts were awarded to Price and Son as main contractors and to the Coalbrookdale Company for the provision of the wrought ironwork. This was in hand when, later in the year, Thomas Groves died. W. N. Swettenham was appointed County Surveyor in his place and he revised the design from independent spans to a three span continuous structure with tubular piles driven to support the foundations. Swettenham wrote to the Coalbrookdale Company, at their Horsehay Works, where the girders were laid out in the yard, asking them to carry out the necessary modifications for £100. As the modifications had to be approved by the Court there were lengthy delays with the girders remaining in the yard. The Coalbrookdale Company declined to quote for these and eventually two fresh contracts were awarded to T. Woodall and Co. of the Windmill Works, Dudley. These were for the piling and fabrication of the piers, the continuous girders, the deck and the parapets.

1887 was, in the meantime, passing rapidly by and there were other troubles. The Great Western Railway claimed that the weir, for which they were responsible had been damaged by the bridgeworks. In October the Magistrates agreed to pay the riparian owner, J. D. Allcroft, who was pressing the Railway Company, a sum of £30 in settlement of his claim. The County Surveyor reported to the October Sessions that work was held up by an unexpected mass of rock which was interfering with the driving of the piles. The delays caused problems with the temporary timber bridge, built by Mr. Treasure, which had to continue to carry the traffic for longer than was originally intended. After calling in an independent valuer Mr. Treasure's claim was eventually settled out of court. No sooner was this dealt with than Price and Son began an action against the County to recover certain balances which they claimed were due to them. The Clerk of the Peace was instructed to take the necessary steps to resist the Action and a settlement was reached for £103. The bridge continues to give good service carrying all the normal trunk road traffic. In the 1950s the wrought iron deck plates were replaced with steel troughing and the transverse or cross beams encased in reinforced concrete.

The Onibury Bridge, replaced by the present structure, was of stone arches and was built by George Edgecombe in 1832, doubtless directed by Stanton on Telford's behalf. Going back a stage further Stanton had problems, in 1831, with the bridge that had to be replaced the following year. With regard to it the Hon. Robert Clive wrote to the Magistrates, at their January 1832 Sessions, to say that "H.M. Government had, with a view to perfecting the intercourse between the two great sea ports of Liverpool and Bristol, established a mail coach on this line of road, which passes twice over Onibury Bridge every night". He went on to say that the Commissioners for the Turnpike disassociated themselves from liability for any accident that might result from the inadequate width of the old bridge.

The River Corve flows past the village of Stanton Lacy, two and a half miles East of Onibury. Access to the village from the Pedlar's Rest - Culmington - Bromfield road, B4365, is over STANTON LACY Bridge. Here in 1821, was a stone bridge of three semicircular arches, each of twelve feet span. Thomas Stanton reported its ruinous condition and the County denied liability, which meant that a new bridge would have to be financed by local subscription. He suggested that a replacement bridge, in the same form, could be built for £150 if the local inhabitants produced the stone. Matthew Stead of Ludlow prepared a drawing and specification, dated 1st March 1826, for a single stone arch bridge of twenty-seven feet span, twelve feet wide. Stanton amended the wing wall layout, in pencil and wrote to Stead that the design would be satisfactory, subject to his pencilled alterations which still remain on the drawing. However on 7th March 1878, the County Surveyor reported the bridge to be still of three semicircular arches and in such poor condition that repairs would cost more than a new bridge. The design was drawn up, for a lattice through girder bridge, of wrought iron on stone abutments. The span was to be forty feet and the width fifteen feet six inches, the deck to be of timber. The wrought iron and timber work were carried out by the Coalbrookdale Company, the same year. There is no record of the main contractor. In 1935 the deck was replaced by one of reinforced concrete.

We must now move Westwards to the village of Bucknell, three miles West of Leintwardine. There are three BUCKNELL Bridges as the River Redlake flows through the village and is crossed and recrossed by the main street. At the West end of the village the road from Chapel Lawn crosses the Redlake on a four ring brick arch bridge of twenty-feet span, at a pretty sharp skew. The rest of the structure is of rubble masonry with flat stone coping to the parapets. These rise to a slight peak at midspan giving the bridge a little extra character. Near the church, in the centre of the village, is an arch bridge of twenty two feet span which may be quite old. However the original structure has been widened on both sides, by extending the arch in reinforced concrete and adding new parapets, spandrels and wing walls of snecked rubble masonry. The result is a pleasing bridge in an attractive setting. At the East end of the village the B4367 road, to Craven Arms, is carried on a bridge of two arches, each of three ring brickwork and fourteen feet span. The rest of the structure is of rubble masonry.

The B4367 road, South of Bucknell, crosses the River Teme half a mile from the village, at LINGEN Bridge. In 1770 a timber horse and footbridge was built at this crossing by a local carpenter named Morris, vehicular traffic having to ford the Teme. In 1828 it was suggested that maintenance and replacement should be a County responsibility and Thomas Stanton was instructed to look into the matter and report. After consideration of his report it was decided that if the "neighbouring noblemen. . . by public subscription" built a carriage bridge the County would come in with a contribution and then take the bridge over. In April 1830 the County Surveyor reported that £150 had been collected and that this would cover the cost of a new horsebridge. The Magistrates authorized a contribution of £150, provided a carriage bridge was built, in accordance with a proper contract, entered into with the local gentry. A contract dated 2nd August 1830 was duly made with James Cole, Builder of Presteign. It appears that this was a popular route for coaches, from Shrewsbury to Knighton, avoiding the steep hills in the vicinity of Clun. The bridge built in 1830 by James Cole consisted of four timber spans, requiring three piers in the river. The two Southernmost piers were of timber while the Northern one was of masonry. The timber superstructure was similar to that invariably used by Telford for his temporary bridges, based on the king post truss. There was also a masonry flood arch behind the North abutment. By 1837 the Teme, which is still a boisterous and destructive stream from the mountains, so damaged the foundations that major repairs were necessary. These were carried out, for £310 by Matthew Stead. In the specification for the repairs a new arch is mentioned though the bridge was still of timber. In fact it was still of timber when an iron structure was first mentioned, in 1860. By 1876 Bucknell was served by a station on the Mid-Wales Railway. It became essential to replace the bridge, barely half a mile from the Station. The stone abutments were still sound and a lattice through girder bridge of two thirty-five foot spans were designed as a permanent replacement. Tenders were invited and that of the Coalbrookdale Company accepted. A temporary ford for vehicles and footbridge were provided while the work was carried out. It was completed by the end of 1877. Though the bridge is more than a hundred years old it remains very much as built. Vehicle weight is restricted to twelve tons. In the late 1950s it was decided that the weakness of the structure was in the cast-iron cross beams supporting the deck plates. A scheme was prepared to strengthen them by attaching pre-stressing tendons to their bottom flanges to make up for the inherent weakness of cast-iron in tension. It will never be known if this, if I may say so, ingenious proposal would have been effective as an unexpected design weakness was discovered in the main girders and so the weight restriction remains.

Travelling up the River Teme from Knighton, along the boundary with Wales, we find a number of bridges spanning the river, of which two are Shropshire responsibilities. The first, LLOYNEY Bridge, is three miles upstream from the town. This is a rather graceful rubble arch bridge of forty feet span. In spite of being of rubble it is well finished with a string course and parapets that rise to a peak at midspan, where there is a small pilaster. The spandrels are pierced by small culverts or tunnels. This bridge has withstood some particularly brutal onslaughts from the unruly Teme, which has made several attempts to cut a new course behind the South abutment. The river's attempts to undercut the North abutment were checked by concrete underpinning in the 1930s.

The second Shropshire responsibility is BEGUILDY Bridge, another four miles upstream. This rubble masonry arch bridge, of twenty-six feet span, was designed by Aaron Hamer, Surveyor to the Bishops Castle Highways Board, in 1871, with the blessing of both Thomas Groves, County Surveyor of Shropshire and of S. W. Williams, County Surveyor of Radnor, both of whose signatures appear on Hamer's drawing.

VI

A Few Early Concrete Bridges

Concrete, in its various forms, cannot really be claimed as a modern invention; the Romans certainly made use of a form of it in their aqueducts and other structures. It was not until very much later, after the discovery of Portland Cement that the development of concrete as a true structural material took place. Earlier concretes were generally filling material and we encountered some examples of this in the previous chapter. The first uses of it structurally were as an alternative to blocks of natural stone. The Royal Engineers were responsible for extensive researches into the benefits of incorporating concrete in the construction of coastal defence forts, in the mid-nineteenth century.

It was not until the means of giving concrete strength in tension, by means of steel reinforcing bars, to match its inherent compressive strength, was introduced, that its real advantages as a structural material were realized. A reinforced concrete bridge was built, crossing the River Waveney near Bungay, in Suffolk, as early as 1870. This was achieved by constructing an arched framework of iron, across the river and embedding it in concrete. However, concrete truly reinforced with scientifically placed steel bars did not appear in this country until the early nineteen hundreds.

In 1909 the demand for a toll-free crossing of the River Severn, in the vicinity of Ironbridge, had become so pressing that the Mayor, Mr. B. Maddox, organized a fund for the purpose which was subscribed to by all classes of society in the district. Lord Forester presented the land required on the Broseley side of the river and Canon Ball, the Lord of the Manor of Madeley, presented the land on that side. The bridge could then be built at Jackfield, half a mile below the Iron Bridge. Due to its freedom from tolls it would be known as the FREE Bridge.

L. G. Mouchel and Partners, one of the leading firms of reinforced concrete consultants, were retained as consultants on this project, the actual designer being Mr. T. Parker. The original drawing was for a bridge of three arches of seventy feet span each. To satisfy the requirements of the Severn Commissioners the central span was enlarged to eighty-seven feet. The reduced side spans were modified into half-arches, springing from the pier but at the crown merging into a horizontal beam, the outer end of which rests on a small concrete abutment on the river bank. The central span would be described as an open spandrel arch. It consists of an arch rib under each parapet, from which vertical struts rise to support the main deck beam. At each vertical strut cross beams span from one main deck beam to the other and support the deck slab. Wrought iron railings form the parapets.

The method of reinforcing all the members with steel bars was referred to, at that time, as the Hennebique System of Ferro-concrete and the contractors for the construction were the Liverpool Hennebique Ferro-concrete Contracting Company. The time taken for construction was six months plus some delay due to flooding. The cost was £1,600, a remarkable example of economy in time and money. During its life the Free Bridge has withstood continuous overloading, occasionally calling for minor remedial work. In 1937 a weight restriction of eight tons was proposed, but this was amended to twelve tons when it was realized that the lower figure would restrict the movement of brewery vehicles in the district. The present limit is ten tons. Brewery waggons come lighter than they did.

A plaque, at the North end of the bridge, states "Haynes Memorial and Subscription Bridge. Cllr. B. Maddox Mayor. 1908-9. Plaque Restored 1955 by descendants of the Haynes family". Though local enquiry produced no knowledge of the Haynes family it is believed that the largest contribution, a sum of £700, was left by a member of the family a one-time native of Ironbridge who had died in Montevideo. If that is not correct I offer my apologies to all concerned.

It is perhaps of interest to note that from a fragmentary correspondence, in the possession of the County Archivist, the Trustees of the Iron Bridge, who stood to suffer serious losses, in tolls, from the opening of the Free Bridge, made strenuous efforts to discourage its use. This included the setting up of a gate, on Lord Foresters land, to which he took some exception. The correspondence ceases with the two parties preparing to go to court.

Although there is no doubt that the Free Bridge is the first bridge in the County to have been built of reinforced concrete, it is equally certain that it was not the first concrete bridge. This honour must go to MYNDTOWN Bridge, a fifteen feet six inches span arch of mass concrete; that is to say, with no reinforcement. The concrete has been used in place of blocks of stone and the whole structure has been cast to give an impression of masonry. Pilasters, string course, coping and chamfered voussoirs in the arch facing rings are all as one would expect in a stone bridge. The date of erection is inscribed, 1906, and the engineer responsible is named as A. Hamer whom we have already met, in the previous chapter, as Surveyor to the Bishops Castle Highways Board, now after the winding up of that authority, Surveyor to the Clun Rural District Council. Myndtown is a hamlet nestling into the Western slopes of the Long Mynd, at its Southern end. The road from Eaton to Myndtown crosses the Criftin Brook over Myndtown Bridge.

In the centre of the village of Minsterley, MINSTERLEY Bridge is a reinforced concrete bridge of thirty feet span over a tributary of the Rea Brook. Sometimes described as an arch, it is in fact a portal frame, that is, the deck is rigidly attached to the abutments giving considerable additional strength to the former. The plaque says that it is a County Bridge, rebuilt in 1909 by A. T. Davis M.I.C.E., County Surveyor.

Three reinforced concrete bridges were built in 1910. Of these NAPELEY LODGE Bridge is over the River Tern and carries the minor road from Norton-in-Hales Eastwards to the B5145. It is sited on the outskirts of the village. The deck of the bridge, which is of fifteen feet span, is slightly arched in the soffit. The parapet on each side appears to have been cast in one piece with the arched end of the slab, the coping, the newels and their caps. This neat little structure is surviving well. PENTRE WERN Bridge carries the Oswestry - Gobowen trunk road, A483, over the River Perry half a mile South of Gobowen. As at Napeley Lodge the soffit of the deck slab is slightly arched, the span being twelve feet. It could easily remain unnoticed as there is no sign of the concrete parapets and the bridge has been very much widened to carry the forty feet width of the trunk road. The third bridge in this trio remains unnoticed most of the time. LITTLE TASKER Bridge carries a rarely used lane leading due West from the Minsterley - Bishops Castle road, A488, half a mile South of the turn for Hyssington Marsh and is over the upper reaches of the River West Onny. This bridge is a very early example of an in-situ T-beam reinforced slab. This provides a lightweight deck which is supported on the brick and stone abutments of an earlier timber bridge. The concrete parapets are cast with some attention to detail, the work being carried out by the Clun Rural District Council. Aaron Hamer may well have been responsible for the design and supervision.

Before 1913 there was a timber bridge of five spans on four timber trestle piers and stone abutments, over the River Severn, to the North of the village of Cressage. It carried the road towards Eaton Constantine, now the B4380. This CRESSAGE Bridge was built in about 1800 as a toll bridge, the Toll House being at the East end. By 1913 the condition of the timber structure gave rise to some concern or possibly the owners found it unprofitable to maintain it. The County Council took it over, extinguished the toll and decided to replace it with a reinforced concrete structure. L. G. Mouchel and Partners were engaged as consultants and prepared the design for a bridge of three segmental arches, the centre span being of eighty feet while the two side spans are of forty feet each. The arches are of hollow construction, the spandrel walls supporting the cross beams which, in turn, support the deck. The parapets are concrete balustrades set to a pleasing camber and the whole structure possesses an elegance which must have suggested great promise for the new material as the basis of an architectural art form, seventy years ago.

The Shrewsbury - Newport road, B5062, crosses the River Roden between the villages of Roden and High Ercall at ERCALL MILL Bridge. This is built on rather different principles from Cressage Bridge and consists of two segmental reinforced concrete arches, of twenty feet span, filled as if they were of masonry. There is no deck, the roadway being supported by the fill. The bridge was built by the County Council in 1915 to replace a brick and stone one of similar dimensions.

A few years later the old masonry bridge, of three twelve feet span arches, carrying the Wellington - Hodnet road, A442, known as WATERS UPTON Bridge, on the West side of the village, was replaced by a reinforced concrete slab bridge of two spans of twenty-one feet each.

The minor road, leaving the A49 trunk road at a point seven miles South of Shrewsbury, into the village of Longnor, crosses the Cound Brook over a multiple box culvert of reinforced concrete, LONGNOR Bridge, built in 1925.

Returning to the North of the county, there is a road that leaves the A5 at Babbinswood, a mile short of Whittington, crosses the River Perry at Perry Farm and goes on to join the Ellesmere - Whittington road, A495, at Maestermyn. PERRY FARM Bridge is a concrete beam and slab bridge of twenty-eight feet span. The reinforcement of the beams is in the form of rolled steel joists embedded in the concrete instead of steel bars. This form is known as composite construction. The bridge was built in the 1920s by the Oswestry Rural District Council and taken over as a County Bridge in 1931. In the 1970s the Severn Trent Water Authority constructed a gauging weir to measure the flow in the River Perry, under the bridge. Unfortunately the necessary excavation struck

Longnor Bridge built in 1925. An early example of the use of concrete in bridge building. This type is known as a multiple box culvert, reinforced concrete bridge. (Photo. A. Blackwall).

New and old Atcham Bridges. John Gwynn's original bridge continued to carry the main A5 until 1929 when the new bridge became operational.

running sand and resulted in massive scour under the foundations of the West abutment which is a monolithic block of concrete. The abutment sank rather more than a foot, carrying the end of the bridge deck down with it, remaining plumb however. That is, the abutment did not tilt during its downward plunge. It was secured at its new level and the bridge now slopes down towards that end. However it was established that everything was perfectly intact and the new inclination of the bridge matched the fall in the road rather better than before; and so it remains.

By 1924 the County Council were concerned about the inadequate width of John Gwynn's beautiful Atcham Bridge when it came to coping with the ever increasing traffic on the Holyhead Road, A5. Widening was instantly rejected with the result that it was agreed that the old bridge should be preserved and by-passed by a new bridge which would carry the trunk road. Gwynn's bridge had been built on the site of the ford by which the road originally crossed the river. The extra width of waterway to compensate for the shallow depth of the ford meant that his bridge measured more than three hundred feet between abutments, twice the normal width of the river. However, due to the alignment of the road and the bend in the river, the new bridge would have to measure more than four hundred and fifty feet between abutments.

The County Surveyor, William Butler took on responsibility for the design and construction of the NEW ATCHAM Bridge and engaged L. G. Mouchel and Partners as consultants. The design took the form of a series of open spandrel arches, slightly reminiscent of, though much larger than, the Free Bridge at Jackfield. The centre span is of one hundred and twenty feet, with two spans of ninety-eight feet and two of fifty-nine feet. Construction was carried out by Messrs. Gray's Ferro-concrete Company. On two occasions, during construction, the Severn flooded and inundated the works, virtually destroying everything in its path. This double setback naturally delayed the completion of the bridge, on which work is believed to have started towards the end of 1927. The opening, as set out on the plaque, was by the Rt. Hon. Herbert Morrison M.P., Minister of Transport, on 24th October 1929. The cost was £52,500 including the roadworks.

The five arches are separated from one-another at deck level by an air gap of about half an inch or so, to allow for temperature expansion. The gaps tend to widen as winter comes on and the concrete shrinks, and to close when summer returns and the concrete warms up and expands. In the days of tar-macadam surfacing, which is a comparatively elastic material, this movement was comfortably accommodated without opening cracks in the road surface. However in more recent times hot-rolled asphalt, which will not stretch, has been used, resulting in the appearance of a crack right across the road, over each pier, towards the end of November each year. It always astonished me how many helpful people did their best to create alarm and despondency by reporting "Dangerous cracks on Atcham Bridge". Of course it is very easy to say that a bridge is unsafe but it is a bridge engineer's responsibility to declare it to be safe and stand or fall by his decision. No doubt it was the same in Telford's time.

During the nineteen thirties a series of more than a dozen reinforced concrete bridges appeared on a line running roughly South West of Shrewsbury. They may be, in the most part, not of exceptional interest, but the number of them, built over a short period, makes them surely worth a mention.

Half a mile North West of Great Hanwood the Rea Brook is spanned by CRUCKTON Bridge, of two eighteen foot spans. It consists of a concrete deck supported on steel beams, the shuttering for the concrete being sheets of corrugated iron which have been left in position. The brick parapets are carried on reinforced concrete beams which conceal the steel beams and corrugated sheeting. It was completed in 1929.

In the village of Stapleton, BRIDGE FARM Bridge, over the Moat Brook, is a concrete slab of thirteen feet six inches span on stone abutments, built in 1933. Continuing down the same road towards Church Pulverbatch the Moat Brook is crossed again at Moat Cottages, attached to Moat Farm. MOAT COTTAGES Bridge is a five feet concrete slab, built in 1931. Six miles to the South West, between the villages of Ratlinghope and Bridges is BRIDGES Bridge, a reinforced concrete box culvert, of ten feet span, built in 1931. The next reinforced concrete bridge is about a mile away to the West, between Bridges and Kinnerton. KINNERTON Bridge is another box culvert of slightly greater span, built in 1934 over the Kinnerton Brook. Half a mile East of Wentor, at Prolley Moor on the road to Asterton, is PROLLEY MOOR Bridge which is a slab supported on concrete beams, twelve feet six inches in span over the Criftin

Brook. It was built in 1930 by the Clun Rural District Council. A mile Southwards, down the Criftin Brook is CRIFTIN Bridge; unlike all the others in this catalogue of minor concrete bridges this is a mass concrete arch of thirteen feet span, which may mean that it belongs to this period or it could be twenty years older. The finish is excellent and with no reinforcement to rust, split off pieces of concrete surface and spread brown stains, it looks as new.

We must now move six miles South to Kempton, where the road from the village to Purslow crosses the River Kemp over KEMPTON Bridge. This is a concrete beam and slab bridge of seventeen feet span, with neat concrete parapets, built in 1930. The next bridge is a rather larger one, built in 1935. This is CLUNGUNFORD Bridge which carries the B4367 road to Abcott and Hopton Heath. It replaces an ancient timber bridge of three ten feet spans on stone piers. We next move eight miles North West to CEFN EINION Bridge which is another fairly substantial structure of beams and slab, of twenty feet span over the River Unk, supported on concrete abutments. The parapets are of brick and it was built in 1937. From the village of Cefn Einion we move some five miles to the South West, to the South bank of the River Clun, where a tributary coming from the Black Mountain joins the river. A minor road follows the brook down the valley and crosses it over COW HALL Bridge, consisting of two five feet span slabs, built in 1936. A little over two miles South of Cow Hall is the hamlet of Cwm Collo where the Hurgin Brook, a tributary of the Teme is spanned by CWM COLLO Bridge, a fourteen feet span slab built in 1938. Half a mile downstream from there the Wain Brook joins it having been crossed by CWMBRAIN Bridge, very similar to the previous one and built at the same time. Finally we follow the Hurgin Brook for half a mile, almost to its outfall into the Teme, in the hamlet of Melinagrogue. MELINAGROGUE Bridge is a ten foot slab also built in 1938.

There were other minor concrete bridges built, during this period, in the rest of the County but I have listed these, in the South West because they indicate a regular plan and are largely due to the drive and enthusiasm of the local Surveyor on the County Staff, Thomas E. Mackie, M.I.C.E.

Still in the nineteen thirties, we will look at a major reinforced concrete structure over the River Severn between Alveley and Highley, six miles below Bridgnorth. It was not built by the County but by the Highley Mining Company and ultimately transferred to the County by the National Coal Board, on the closure of the colliery.

In 1936 the Mining Company decided that a bridge was required to connect the Alveley Pit, on the East of the river, to the Highley Pit, on the West, which was served by the Severn Valley Railway. A design was prepared by the British Reinforced Concrete Engineering Company (B.R.C.) This was for a continuous structure supported on two abutments and two intermediate piers, forming a central span of one hundred and fifty feet and two side spans of fifty feet each. As the purpose of the bridge was to carry two narrow gauge tub tracks it consists, in principle, of two separate concrete girders, nine feet apart, varying in depth from three feet at midspan and at the abutments to eighteen feet over the piers. This results in a pleasingly curved soffit line. Each girder carried its own tub track and

Alveley Pit Bridge. Now used as a footpath but originally built by the Highley Mining Company to carry two narrow gauge tub tracks.

a light deck was provided at either side of the tracks for colliery personnel to walk. The contractors were Messrs. Thomas Beighton Ltd. and operations started on the site on 30th June 1936. Details of the construction work are clearly explained in an article by A. P. Mason in the August 1937 edition of the magazine *Concrete and Constructional Engineering.* It was completed in June 1937 at a cost of £6,000.

The bridge gave good service up to the final closure of the colliery in the nineteen sixties when the National Coal Board handed it over, for a nominal figure, to the County Council. Though access to the bridge is straightforward from Alveley, it is virtually inaccessible to vehicles from the public highway at the Highley end. The Severn Valley Railway line has to be crossed, followed by a sheer drop of between fifty and a hundred feet down to the river. A further complication is that the deck of the bridge was not designed for vehicular loading, but only for pedestrians. The public use of the bridge therefore becomes a problem and at the time of writing is reduced to use as a footbridge and as a means of getting a water main and telephone cables across the river.

While on this side of the County we might note two reinforced concrete arches carrying the Telford - Kidderminster road A442. The first is WORFE Bridge, two miles North of Bridgnorth and the other, slightly smaller, is BLUNDER Bridge, a brick arch widened on both sides in reinforced concrete, as with Harley Bridge. It is six miles South of Bridgnorth. Mention of these two concrete arches brings us to another one contemporary with them. MIDDLETON Bridge carries the Ludlow - Bridgnorth road B4364, over the Ledwyche Brook a couple of miles North East of Ludlow. It is a reinforced concrete arch of twenty-four feet span, built in 1937, to replace an old arch that had been worked on by Thomas Stanton in the 1820s.

We now come to one of the last important reinforced concrete bridges to be built in the County before the general use of pre-stressed concrete. CRUDGINGTON Bridge, carrying the Shrewsbury - Newport road, B5062 over the River Tern was, prior to 1940, an ancient, possibly sixteenth century, red sandstone bridge of four ribbed arches. Replacement became urgent and a reinforced concrete open spandrel arch bridge of about one hundred and twenty feet span, was designed. When excavation commenced on site it became clear that the subsoil survey had been misleading and, due to the presence of glacial silt deteriorating to running sand, foundations suitable for an arch of the proportions proposed would be out of the question. A re-design had to be urgently undertaken. Fortunately there was no contractor involved, the work being carried out by direct labour, as has been the case in the majority of bridges built in the County for some time.

The design that emerged was of a three span balanced cantilever bridge; that is to say that the structure is continuous with the whole weight being borne by the two piers, the outer ends of the shore spans converge with the abutments but are not supported by them. The superstructure is in the form of a hollow box with a nicely curved soffit line. As by this time World War II was getting under way, funds were only available for enough bridge to carry half the road widths. For post-war financial reasons the building of the second half was not contemplated until 1963. It is said that an American visitor was fishing the River Tern in 1940 and struck up a friendly relationship with the bridge gang and particularly with the Foreman, Mr. Edward Freeman. By chance the visitor arranged a second fishing holiday on the Tern in 1963, and was amazed to find work still continuing at the bridge under the direction of Mr. Freeman. His comment apparently was "Gee, I didn't think even the Pyramids took that long".

We have investigated in some detail the foundations of many of the older bridges and it may be of interest to look at the way the foundations were established for this bridge, in order to overcome the treachery of the running sand. The method was developed by the engineer in charge of the construction of the 1940 half of the bridge, the late H. R. Ward, M.I.C.E. As I occupied that position for the 1963 half I followed the same principles. First a sheet pile box, as wide as the pier, was driven into the sand, the piles going well down. Then inside the box a large diameter concrete tube was stood on end and allowed to sink. Sand was removed from inside the tube until it had sunk almost out of sight when a second tube was placed on top. The process was continued until the column of tubes declined to go down any further, in fact firm dry sand had been reached. The hollow column was then filled with concrete. As many concrete filled columns as could be contained in the sheet pile box were established in this way and the pier founded on the platform so formed. I would point out that this is not exactly an orthodox method of establishing bridge foundations but it suited the extreme conditions. The complexity of the site work in building this bridge serves as an example of the reason why factory-made pre-stressed beams caught on so successfully in the post-war years. The cost of setting up hundreds of square yards of timber shuttering, supported on a forest of beams and props and fixing within it tens of thousands of pieces of reinforcement as a labour intensive site operation, leading up to the pouring of the concrete, had become astronomical. To purchase pre-fabricated beams, cast in the cost-efficient atmosphere of the workshop, place them across the gap between the abutments with a suitable mobile crane and then establish the deck on top of them is bound to make cost-effective sense.

VII

The Borough Bridges

Much has been published about the Shrewsbury Town Bridges, over the River Severn, and visitors can, with little trouble, arrange to take a walk along the Severn tow path in the company of an accredited guide and learn about the bridges in the pleasantest possible way. However, in the interests of the completeness of this little volume may we take a brief look at each, in the order of their dates of construction.

On this basis the WELSH Bridge qualifies as our first candidate. But before looking at the present bridge, built in 1795, we must spare a thought for its predecessor. The first Welsh Bridge was sited a few yards upstream of the present one and was approached down Mardol. To look into its history I recommended E. Jervoise's *Ancient Bridges of Wales and Western England.* Here we find that in King Henry the Second's time it was referred to as St. George's Bridge, due to its proximity to St. George's Hospital, Frankwell. The date of construction is not recorded as the bridge must have been developed over a period originating in medieval times. John Leland in his *Itinerary,* written in 1539, speaks of six stone arches and gate houses at both ends, one of them being a "Great Tower". By Leland's time a row of small shops had been built onto the centre of the bridge, replacing a public convenience which had fallen into decay. One of the spans was a drawbridge made of timber. A hundred years later orders were given for the houses on the bridge to be repaired so that they could be let to the greatest advantages, possibly as residential property. By 1660 both the towers were falling down and had to be repaired. One tower survived until shortly before the bridge was replaced by the present structure. Traces of the old bridge can still be found on Frankwell Quay opposite the lower end of Mardol.

As the work on Montford Bridge, carried out by John Carline and John Tilley for Thomas Telford, drew to a close in 1792 the Corporation of the Borough of Shrewsbury invited proposals from bridge builders for the design and construction of a new Welsh Bridge. Carline and Tilley had obviously learned much from their recent experience under the watchful eye of Matthew Davidson

Welsh Bridge built in 1795 downstream of the earlier Saint George's Bridge of which little remains.

and working to Telford's design. As a result their proposal was the one accepted. Telford would have had to no jurisdiction over bridges in the Borough, but Carline and Tilley must have consulted him as it is recorded that he advised against the siting of the bridge in its present position due to eddies and the risk of scour to the foundations. There is still a tendency for the Severn to scour under the pier foundations, providing regular work for an engineering diver.

Carline and Tilley's design was for a bridge of five stone arches, two hundred and sixty-six feet long, rather shorter than the earlier bridge. Detail of the finish must owe much to Montford Bridge. The finish of the arches and of the string course are almost identical, though the spandrels are inset and the parapets are fine balustrades. Grinshill stone was used for all dressed work. At a later date elegant lamp standards were mounted on the parapets, over each pier.

As soon as work was completed on the Welsh Bridge, at a cost of £8,000, and no doubt on the strength of its successful completion, Carline and Tilley were offered the contract to build a single arch bridge of forty feet span over the Rea Brook just before its confluence with the Severn. This is LONGDEN COLEHAM Bridge. The contract was signed by John Tilley and was for £450, the completion date was set at 1st November 1795. The specification calls for Grinshill stone and mentions a puddled clay backing for the arch, as waterproofing, and also "a counter arch over the main arch" which suggests spandrel vaulting. The present parapet railings are a substitution for the original stone parapets. A slight increase in width was achieved, when the railings were set up by corbelling out from the spandrels to support the plinth course on which the railings are set up. Recent impact damage to the plinth course necessitated the purchase of a few cubic feet of dressed stone. Bearing in mind the price for which this bridge was built (£450), it is perhaps interesting to note that if it was to be built today, of the same stone as that used for the repair, the cost of the stone alone would be approaching a quarter of a million pounds. Perhaps this explains why we are not able to build public highway bridges of dressed stone today.

The next bridge to be built carries the railway line and a portion of Shrewsbury Station over the river. In 1848 the Shrewsbury and Birmingham Railway was in the course of construction and SHREWSBURY STATION Bridge, a stone viaduct, four of whose seven arches are over the river, was built under the direction of Robert Stephenson and his assistant Joseph Locke. The construction of this line, which was not completed until some time later, was one of the last railway projects of Robert Stephenson's career.

In 1903 the track over the river was quadrupled and the station extended over the river. To carry this increase the stone viaduct was widened in steel girder construction. The outer edges of the widened deck are supported on Pratt truss girders, which consist of a series of letter "Ns". The weight carried by these girders is mainly that of station platforms. The additional tracks are carried on deep and massive plate web girders. All the steelwork is rivetted together, this

Greyfriars Bridge opened on New Year's Day 1880 and links Longden Coleham with Saint Julian's Friars.

method being at the height of its popularity at the time and not for some years to be replaced by welding. The widening is in two spans carried on cast-iron columns in midstream.

In the eighteen seventies, while protracted discussions and negotiations were taking place regarding the establishment of a privately owned toll bridge, in the Kingsland or Belle Vue area, the Borough decided to go ahead with the construction of a footbridge linking Longden Coleham with Saint Julian's Friars. This GREYFRIARS Bridge, is in the form of a hog-backed Pratt truss, though more frequently referred to as a lattice girder. It was completed in time to be opened on New Year's Day 1880, the material used gives the impression of wrought iron. It was claimed, by the foundry where the sections were produced, that they were tested to a maximum tensile stress of twenty-two tons per square inch, which would certainly be an acceptable figure for this material. The footbridge, whose span is one hundred and fifty feet, was built by the Cochrane Engineering Company of Dudley for £2500.

In the meantime planning for the construction of a toll bridge continued and in 1873 a Bill was promoted in Parliament for the statutory authority, required by an organization which is not a highway authority, to build a bridge over a navigable waterway. A second Bill was promoted and passed in 1880. It is recorded that the driving force behind the project was Thomas Charles Townsend. The engineer however, was Henry Robertson, the M.P. for Shrewsbury. It is possible that the siting of Shrewsbury School, after its move

Kingsland Toll Bridge constructed by the same company that built the bridge below Victoria Falls. (Photo. A. Blackwall).

Port Hill Footbridge. A traditional suspension bridge built in 1922 by David Rowell & Co. of Westminster. (Photo. A. Blackwall).

from the centre of the town, may have had some influence upon the conception and siting of KINGSLAND TOLL Bridge.

The contract for its construction was awarded to the Cleveland Bridge and Engineering Company of Darlington, a company still of world-wide renown, whose bridges may be found in all parts of the world, particularly in India and Africa. A well known example of their work is the bridge below the Victoria Falls. The Stockton Forge Company is also mentioned, presumably in connection with the rolling of the sections used in the construction. The Kingsland Bridge is in the form of a two hinged arch of two hundred and twelve feet span. The deck is suspended between the two arch ribs; at midspan it is below the crown of the arch but near the abutments it is supported above the ribs. Costing £11,156 it is an elegant structure with high quality masonry in the abutments and end portals. In times of flood it has been known for both the English and Welsh Bridges to become impassable, leaving Kingsland Bridge, with its high level deck and approaches, to save the day for traffic approaching Shrewsbury from anywhere but the North.

PORT HILL FOOTBRIDGE is a vital link across the Severn for pedestrians from the Port Hill and Copthorne areas, making their way into town and benefitting, at the same time, from a pleasant walk through the Quarry. Nevertheless it has always been taken completely for granted except on two nights of the year. The final event of both days of Shrewsbury Flower Show, in the Quarry, is invariably a magnificent firework display. As soon as this is over hundreds, if not thousands, of visitors start to make their way back to their coaches, parked somewhere in Copthorne. All are determined not to keep their coach waiting. A couple of gallant policemen attempt to stem the rush onto the bridge, knowing that the exit at the far end is restricted by the paying-in turnstiles by which the visitors had entered earlier in the day. All involved are struck by a sudden fear as to the bridge's ability to carry such a concentrated mass of humanity. Questions and recriminations continue for some time. A survey and analysis of the structure, some years ago, showed that then it was strong enough, explaining perhaps why it had never fallen into the river. However I understand that recent investigations suggest some attention to the suspension cables which are now about sixty years old.

This is a traditional suspension bridge with steel wire cables (two each side) in the place of the chains of earlier designs. A most important feature in the design of a suspension bridge is that the deck should possess longitudinal rigidity. As the cables are suspended freely across the river, if the deck is lacking in stiffness, the whole structure would writhe about uncontrollably, under the effect of loading or the wind blowing through it. Port Hill Footbridge is adequately stiffened in this respect by its lattice girder parapets. The bridge which measures some two hundred feet between suspension towers, was built by David Rowell and Company of Westminster, in 1922 and opened on 18th January 1923. The cost was £2,600 of which £2,000 was donated by the Shropshire Horticultural Society.

The English Bridge was designed by John Gwynn (a native of Shrewsbury) in 1768. In 1921 A. W. Ward M.I.C.E. redesigned Gwynn's original to reduce the steep incline and widen the road to its present proportions. (Photo. A. Blackwall).

The history of the ENGLISH Bridge would call for much intensive research if it was not for the beautifully set out brochure, prepared for the Royal opening of the present structure, in 1927, price one shilling. In fact the Royal opening by the Prince of Wales never took place, due to a sudden death, calling for Court Mourning, at the time. A little while later Queen Mary drove over the bridge in her monumental Daimler, without any ceremony. The site engineer took a photograph of the occasion, which he gave me many years later. It is now in the possession of the County Archivist. The historical section of the brochure is the work of H. E. Forrest, F.L.S. and will now be our main source of information.

It appears from the records of disputes between the Abbey and the Town, concerning the maintenance of the earliest bridge at this crossing, that the latter was built by the Abbot, probably at the same time as the building of the Abbey, which would be in Norman times. This bridge consisted of five stone arches over the river and a raised causeway carried on twelve timber-decked spans on stone piers, continuing up into Abbey Foregate, to a point above flood level. Towards the East end of the main structure was a massive gate tower, with a gate and drawbridge and accommodation for the gate keeper. There was also accommodation for prisoners. In 1546 the tower collapsed under the force of a great flood but the prisoner awaiting judgement, for felony, miraculously escaped injury and so was pardoned. The bridge, which was known at this time as the Stone Bridge, carried a number of houses and shops. Even without these it was extremely narrow and in 1765 a subscription was opened to pay for the Act of Parliament required for widening. An order was made to demolish the tower, which by this time had little purpose to serve, the drawbridge having already been done away with. It proved to consist of much ecclesiastical masonry including the statues of three saints.

Sufficient money having been raised to finance the widening, this was started on 9th June 1767, by Edward Smythe of Acton Burnell laying the first stone. The plan had been prepared by a Mr. Mylne. The following year, however, the design for a new bridge was put forward by John Gwynn whom we have already met, at Atcham, in Chapter 1. He was an architect who had been born in Shrewsbury but practised in London. This was accepted. There must have been great difficulties encountered with the widening. A fresh start was therefore made on 29th June 1769 by Sir John Astley, Bart., who had contributed £1,000 towards it, laying the first stone. Work had already started on Gwynn's bridge at Atcham in 1768. Sir John Astley's first stone for the English Bridge contained a copper plate on which was engraved (in Latin) "In the reign of George The Third, the father of his country, Sir John Astley, Bart., on the 29th of June 1769 in the Mayoralty of Edward Vaughan Esq., laid this first stone of a work designed for the Public Utility, and for the Ornament of the Town, and which was first begun by the great Munificence of the said Sir John Astley, the Right Honourable Lord Clive, Thomas Hill Esq., and the Corporation of Shrewsbury; and which, under the divine favour, is to be completed by the extraordinary and voluntary liberality of many other public spirited persons, Mr. John Gwynn, a native of this Town, being the Architect".

This bridge, consisting of seven semicircular arches, making a total length of four hundred feet, was completed and opened to traffic in 1774, at a cost of about £16,000. It was an occasion for some rejoicing as the new bridge was free of tolls, unlike its predecessor which must have been a toll bridge. Gwynn's agent, on this site, was the Shrewsbury-born architect who also practised in Shrewsbury, William Hayward.

Not long after its completion the new bridge came in for some criticism due to the gradient of the roadway up to the crown of the central arch which had been purposely built high so as to provide good headroom for navigation. From time to time proposals were put up to ease the gradients of the roadway over the bridge, particularly with the falling off of the volume of river traffic.

In 1921 A. W. Ward, M.I.C.E., the Borough Surveyor, put the design of the present bridge before the Corporation. This was for a stone bridge of seven arches, just as Gwynn's was, but the central semicircular arch was to be reconstructed as a segmental arch, with the first five feet of voussoirs, up from the springing, eliminated. The crown of the arch would then be five feet lower. The three arches on either side of the central arch were lowered in proportion, the landward arches remaining semicircular. Thus the gradient of the roadway from the ends of the bridge to the centre was eased by five feet. Also all the masonry of the arches and spandrels could be re-used, in the same relationship, provided the stone was still sound. A quantity of additional arch voussoirs and stones for the abutments and piers was required as the new bridge was to be fifty feet wide against the twenty-three feet six inches width of the old bridge.

Work started with the construction of a timber and steel temporary bridge, immediately upstream, to carry highway traffic while the reconstruction was going on. The old bridge was completely dismantled and all the stones to be re-used carefully numbered. In December 1926 a stone in a relative position to the one of 1769, with a cavity containing the old copper plate of that occasion and a new one, inscribed (once again in Latin) "In the seventeenth year of King George the Fifth, by the Grace of God King of the British Dominions, Defender of the Faith, Emperor of India, this famous bridge, called formerly the Stone Bridge, but today the English Bridge, being too narrow for those who cross it, was widened by twenty-six and a half feet at the expense of the Nation, the County and the Borough, and rebuilt by the inhabitants of Shrewsbury, Henry Heywood Heywood-Lonsdale being Chairman of the Salop County Council, Richard Devereux Bromley, Mayor for the second time, and Arthur Walburgh Ward, Engineer. A.D. 1926". The piers of the old bridge had been founded on layers of timber planks laid on the gravel, at a shallow depth, as was the normal practice at that time. Foundations for the new bridge are of concrete, placed twenty feet below summer water level in a stratum of firm clay. This, together with a concrete saddle laid over the back of each arch, was the only concrete used, making the English Bridge one of the last major bridges, if not the last, to be built of stone. It is during recent years that the price of dressed stone as a bridge building material has become prohibitive. The cost of the English Bridge in 1926 was £86,000. It is hard to imagine what it would have cost at today's prices.

This leaves us with three modern bridges to look at. The first to be built was CASTLE WALK Footbridge, in 1951, and already over thirty years old. It is a concrete bridge some two hundred and fifty feet long and consists of two cantilevers supporting a midspan section. That is to say that, on each of the two supporting piers is a hollow box girder, of concrete, the greatest depth being over the pier but tapering towards midspan and towards the bank. The bank end is held down while that over the river is shaped so that it can support the end of the central section which is also a hollow box. It will not be difficult to appreciate that the two cantilevers, supporting the centre section, will tend to droop under its weight. This will put the upper fibres of the cantilever boxes into tension. At the same time the lower fibres of the centre section will be put into tension. To counteract these stresses high tensile steel cables are run from end to end of the bridge and are arranged so as to run through the upper part of the cantilever boxes and through the lower part of the centre section box. Tension is applied to the cables by hydraulic jacks, stretching them. The ends of the stretched cables are firmly clamped to the ends of the concrete members before the jacks are released. On the release of the jacks the cables try to resume their normal length, applying compression to the areas of concrete hitherto in tension and so neutralizing that tension. This is a great over-simplification of the basic principles of pre-stressing but, hopefully, may be of some value to the completely uninitiated. The idea is to make concrete members stronger without increasing their size. The result here is a slender structure with smooth, gently curving lines and, in 1951 it was a comparatively advanced design and the first of its type in Shropshire.

Almost a mile downstream from Castle Walk TELFORD WAY Bridge carries the new road of that name over the river. This concrete bridge is built on very much the same principles as the previous one. Instead of a hollow box there are six pre-stressed solid concrete beams supporting a reinforced concrete deck. Each beam consists of three parts, two cantilevers supported on piers on the river banks and a central section supported by the cantilevers. On the East side of the river, the element of the cantilever projecting back over the land is greatly extended and so provides a flood relief opening, as required by the River Authority. The gently curved soffit and slender piers again give the bridge a simple and pleasing elevation. It was opened on 25th June 1964, having cost £450,000.

Finally the newest bridge, FRANKWELL Footbridge, situated two hundred yards upstream of the Welsh Bridge, provides an invaluable pedestrian link between Frankwell car park and the Town Centre, *via* the Riverside Shopping Arcade. Built by the Borough Corporation this bridge was the subject of an Act of Parliament promoted by the Authority. It was designed, for the Borough, by the well-known firm of consulting engineers, Mott Hay and Anderson. It represents a very up-to-date form of bridge design, frequently seen on the Continent, especially in Germany and becoming more common in this country. It is of steel and concrete, the slender deck being supported at two points in the main span by inclined cables passing through the top of the concrete tower on the Frankwell bank and anchored into the ground. The Frankwell end of the deck passes through the tower and terminates on a simple abutment, while the town end of the bridge is supported on a column on the river bank and continues over Smithfield Road. The bridge is thus a form of cantilever but the type is generally referred to as cable-stayed suspension bridge. By any name it is an extremely elegant structure and well-built by the Bovis Construction Company which is related to the P. and O. Shipping Line. The cost was of the order of £350,000.

These then are the bridges, built and maintained by the Borough Corporation, (with the exception of Kingsland Toll Bridge, of course) and added, with respect, to this little book of County Bridges.

Appendix 1
The Restoration of the Iron Bridge

From 1950, when the County Council took the Iron Bridge over, regular measurements were taken of the distance, between the front corners of the two cast-iron base plates, from which the two ends of the main arch spring, across the river. This was to establish the belief that the two abutments were being squeezed

The Iron Bridge. The design was originally inspired by Thomas Farnolls Pritchard and finally developed under the direction of Abraham Darby III.

together and the arch crushed. As these span measurements were obtained by stretching a lightweight steel tape-measure across the river and pulling it tight we could not hope for an accuracy nearer than an eighth to a quarter of an inch, because of the catenery or sag in the tape and wind vibration. The annual movement that we were attempting to check, however, was less than an eighth of an inch. So, to monitor the movement realistically, measurements had to be taken over a period of years, until a significant degree of movement was established. Another source of inaccuracy could be the effect of changes in temperature on the length of the tape which was of the common type, made of Carbon steel and susceptible to temperature variations. To eliminate the effect of this as far as possible the same tape was used each time and measurements were always taken under the same climatic conditions, that is, in still air at about 40°F. These conditions are not difficult to find on a foggy day in February. For some reason we never considered getting hold of a, more sophisticated, Invar steel tape which would have been less sensitive to temperature effects.

Between 1950 and 1960 the span measurements became shorter by about an inch and in that time a number of new fractures in the cast-iron members was recorded. Nearly all were in the Northern half of the arch. Only one fracture has been recorded after 1960. All the main ribs and deck beams remained intact. The precise analysis of the distribution of stress among the various members making up the arch would be a highly complex and time-consuming operation and rather beyond the resources available. The outcome would be perhaps of limited, academic interest and it was never seriously considered. Maybe one day it will be undertaken as a student exercise, backed by the computer resources of a university with the time to do it. The approach to the problem had therefore to be the consideration of external forces affecting the structure and the possbility of resisting them or isolating the bridge from them. As these were mainly the effects of earth pressure, geological investigations were indicated.

There had been, a few years previously, an abortive proposal to build a modern steel bridge, alongside the Iron Bridge, as a vehicular by-pass. In connection with this proposal an extensive range of boreholes had been drilled across the valley and the information they had produced was now very useful. The bedrock on both sides of the valley slopes gently towards the centre of the river and could be located at about thirty feet below the top of the river bank. The whole mass of earth on the valley sides might be moving down the slope of the bedrock, bringing completely imponderable forces to bear on the bridge. As the bedrock was described as mudstone in the borehole reports and it is known to deteriorate into slippery clay, under certain wet conditions, this could well be so. On the other hand these forces might be limited to localized earth pressures near the surface which could be checked or diverted.

At the many meetings, involving the County and Government Departments there began to be a division between those who believed that the bridge must be isolated from the forces which they felt to be irresistible and those who believed the forces which were crushing the bridge were finite, calculable and capable of being stopped. However checks on the structure of the North abutment showed that sagging and bulging stonework was pressing on the ironwork of the arch and was responsible for the many fractures noted in that area. It appeared therefore that attention to this should be the first priority.

Many suggestions were put forward at the various meetings. One suggestion which was followed up was that the County should engage the services of a recognized consulting engineer who would not be influenced by either of the conflicting views held by the engineers so far concerned. His fee would be equally shared by the County and the two Government Departments, the Ministry of Works and the Ministry of Transport. The latter Ministry had, over the years, agreed to treat the Iron Bridge as if it carried a classified road and paid out grants towards routine maintenance and so were able to contribute in this situation. Haddon C. Adams, a well-known figure in the world of bridge design and who was known to have a particular interest in the Bridge, was invited and engaged as Consultant. In 1965 he started to prepare his report and recommendations, using the data and measurements gathered by the County Bridge Section over the past fifteen years.

The Adams Report, prepared in the offices of Messrs. Sandford, Fawcett, Wilton and Bell, was submitted to the County in the late summer of 1966. This proposed routine maintenance only to the North abutment; the two side spans, on the South bank, were to be demolished and replaced by something resembling the original South abutment, but in the form of a hollow box. The main arch was to be isolated from external horizontal forces by freeing one end of the arch ribs at the springing. The abutments could then continue to move together, under earth pressures, without damaging the iron arch structure. Reaction to this Report, at the Shire Hall, was favourable with reservations. There were serious doubts as to whether the sound principles of the proposal could be achieved without seriously endangering the whole structure, in the process. The Severn River Authority expressed their firm objections to the Restoration of the South abutment to its 1779 form, on the grounds that such action would impair the existing flood capacity of the bridge. At the invitation of the Ministry of Transport the Cementation Company's Foundations Division suggested that the rate of movement in relation to the foundation pressures, imposed by the weight of the abutments, implied that the forces involved were limited. In fact an increase of foundation pressure, onto the bedrock, of a little under half a ton per square foot, would check the movement. This could be applied by means of stressed anchorage cables fixed to the abutments. Four anchorage cables, down into the bedrock, would be required at each abutment and each cable would need to be stressed to one hundred tons. Mr. Adams felt that this would be disastrous to the bridge. It was agreed, however, that boreholes should be sunk to investigate the feasibility of this proposal.

At this time it was appreciated that funds in excess of £100,000 would have to be raised to cover the restoration in whatever form it took. The Ministry of Transport made it quite clear that the grants which had been made towards routine maintenance could not be stretched towards a sum of this magnitude. Equally it was agreed that it would impose an intolerable burden on the County rates. The only solution would be some form of fund raising. The late Lord Bridgeman was approached and agreed to be chairman of a fund raising committee, to be formed as soon as all the technical details were agreed between the parties concerned.

Early in 1968 the Cementation Company drilled boreholes through the abutments, into the bedrock beneath. The evidence produced indicated that the stressed anchorage proposal was feasible from a geological point of view. Opinion seemed equally divided between Mr. Adam's and the Cementation Company's proposals. In September 1968 it was agreed to ask Mr. Adams to reconsider some of the recommendations in his report. However, by this time Haddon C. Adams was a sick man, never to return to the drawing board. He would dearly have loved to see his proposals to the Iron Bridge coming to fruition as a climax to his long and distinguished career. In my young days the text books he wrote were the foundation of many a chartered engineer's career, especially on the subject of reinforced concrete.

It was agreed between the Ministries and the County that Messrs. Sandford Fawcett, Wilton and Bell be invited to carry out the re-appraisal which would have been done by Mr. Adams had he been able. Mr. J. A. Williams, one of the Partners, took on this task which amounted to the writing of a fresh Report. Like Mr. Adams he worked in close consultation with the County Bridge Office. He also consulted the Severn River Authority in August 1969. Following this he invited the interested parites to meet and share his thoughts and hear his intentions. Once again opinions were divided between the "involvement of infinite external forces" theory which had been the basis of Mr. Adam's Report and "positive resistance to calculable forces" which was first put up by the Cementation Company and now included, in principle, with other suggestions in Mr. Williams' Report. In October 1969 he issued his Draft Report containing a wide range of proposals. In the discussions that followed it became established that neither Mr. Adams' original proposal nor the stressed anchorage was acceptable as both were considered to contain unknown factors which might lead to trouble. The Cementation Company's contention that the external forces could be assessed and stopped was however retained as a basic premise. One of Mr. Williams' proposals involved the classic principle of strutting the abutments apart, across the bed of the river. The implications were examined in great detail and it was learnt that the Ministry of Transport Bridge Engineering Technology Division had recently applied this form of strutting to Weldon Bridge, over the River Coquet in Northumberland. Here the strut took the form of a reinforced concrete invert, laid below the bed of the river, joined to rigid vertical walls facing the existing masonry abutments. What was provided, in fact, was positive resistance to movement with known force by means of a structure of known strength, with a comfortable safety factor. This then should be the method and form for stopping the movement at the Iron Bridge. When this proposal had been accepted, in principle, by all concerned the implications of what it would involve were fully investigated. The cost of extensive coffer dams, which would be required, to instal the reinforced concrete strut beneath the river bed, became a major concern. Coffer dams are formed of interlocking steel sheet piles, driven into the river bed and held upright by massive steel or timber frames. The possibility of applying some form of prefabricated strut, which could be floated in position, lowered to a trench in the river bed and fixed in position by divers, was hopefully put forward as a more economical alternative. This eventually had to be rejected as such a strut would have to be set higher up the abutments than the invert and would constitute an obstruction in the river.

It was therefore agreed that Mr. Williams should go ahead with the detail design as soon as the depth at which the invert slab should be set, in the bed of the river, had been agreed with the Severn River Authority. As a large number of sheet piles would have to be driven, to form the coffer dams, the County agreed to drive some test piles, in the vicinity of the bridge so that the vibration experienced by the structure could be assessed. The County Special Works Division pitched and drove the test piles under the watchful eyes and instruments of two subdivisions of the Works Ministry. The seismograph registered negligible movement, in the structure, from the vibration of pile driving. Surprisingly a marked rhythmic movement was recorded, after the pile driving had finished and the only activity on the bridge was a little old lady walking across, carrying a shopping basket. One thing that this achieved was to bear out the contention that the bridge was deficient in diagonal sway bracing and tended to rock from side to side, under rhythmic impact, even as light as this. It would be feasible, however to go ahead with the proposed coffer dams when the time came to carry out that part of the operation.

By this time the Government Department involved in the project had become the Directorate of Ancient Monuments, part of the Department of the Environment (DOE) and I was able to report to a meeting, between the Directorate and the County that the method of preserving the Iron Bridge was agreed at engineer level. The order of cost appeared to be in the region of £135,000. This would have to be produced by voluntary fund raising with, it was hoped, contributions from the Treasury, on behalf of the Directorate, and from the County. The proposed size of the County's contribution was arrived at by means of a simple formula, suggested at one of the meetings. This was that if the restoration was not carried out the bridge would deteriorate until it reached the stage of becoming a public danger. In this case the County might have to face the responsibility of demolishing it in the interests of public safety. The estimated cost of this operation, £20,000, was then accepted as a reasonable figure for the County's contribution.

Following the excellent work by The Royal Engineers in preventing the collapse of the Britannia Railway Bridge, over the Menai Straits, after damage by fire, the idea of seeking their help with the Iron Bridge was put forward. It was proposed that they might undertake the lightening and strengthening of the North abutment, with materials supplied by the County, as a "Military Aid to Civil Community" operation. This, it was hoped, would keep the cost to a minimum. However, objections from both employers and trades unions in the construction industry were received and accepted and the idea was not followed on. The 'Sappers' were naturally disappointed at missing what might have been an interesting challenge, but their Commanding Officer commented that at least the County Surveyor, the Engineer in charge of the County Special Works Division and the Bridge Engineer were all one-time officers in the Royal Engineers.

It had been decided to refer to the work on the North abutment as Phase I, the installing of the strutting invert slab under the river bed as Phase II and the tidying up of the whole structure and its environment as Phase III. It was hoped that after the completion of Phases I and II the Ancient Monuments Directorate would take the bridge into 'Guardianship', meaning that though it would remain a County Bridge the future financial responsibility would rest with the Treasury.

The question of funding Phases I and II was then seriously considered at a meeting at the Shire Hall, in May 1971, with the late Lord Bridgeman in the chair, as he had promised some years earlier. He was now present, however, in his capacity of President of the recently formed (1968) Ironbridge Gorge Museum Trust. This body had already raised substantial sums for the restoration of relics of the Industrial Revolution in the Ironbridge and Coalbrookdale district. As the Iron Bridge is undoubtedly an important relic of the Industrial Revolution the Chairman brought with him, to the meeting, an established source of fund raising for the project. By this time a change in the system of Government grants, paid to highway authorities, had eliminated the Ministry of Transport, now a section of the DOE, from taking any further part in the restoration.

An important outcome of this meeting was that, in November 1971, the Chairman of the Museum Trust, announced that the Trust had received a contribution towards the Bridge Restoration Project of no less than £50,000. Various conditions were naturally attached to it. One of these was that the Treasury should match this contribution and the County should contribute at least £20,000. Certain differences had arisen between the engineers of the various parties concerning the precise order of the operations in the works programme and further meetings had to be held.

It was agreed that, as the Royal Engineers would not be carrying out Phase I, work on the North abutment would become the responsibility of the County Special Works Division whose normal task was building the structures designed in the Bridge Office. Their record in recent years resulted in there being no hesitation in making this choice. Work was due to start in April 1972 but as late as March of that year there were still outstanding differences, over construction details. These were, however, shelved so that work did start on 15th April 1972.

Work on the North abutment consisted of excavating the filling material from within the structure of the abutment, so as to eliminate many tons of dead weight and leave a hollow masonry box. The roadway, on the bridge, would be carried over this void on a concealed concrete deck, supported on prefabricated concrete beams, which would also act as struts to maintain the existing resistance to the earth pressure, at that level. Until these beams took over, this resistance had to be maintained by means of struts and jacks throughout the operation. The crumbling brick archway, through the abutment, was to be completely encased in reinforced concrete, all of which would be concealed from view when completed. Industrial insurance cover against disaster was taken out due to the uncertainty regarding the stability of the external masonry. If a claim had had to be made against this cover it is quite problematical as to how the money could have been spent.

In the event the work proceeded satisfactorily, in spite of the early discovery that the masonry, which had the appearance of solid walls proved to be, in many areas, only a thin facing covering the rubble filling. Excavation had to be accompanied by the construction of a reinforced concrete lining to preserve the stability of the external masonry; a touch and go operation at times. Nevertheless, by the end of summer, 1972 this work was satisfactorily completed, comfortably within the estimated cost. Some help, in this respect, came from the co-operation of the statutory undertakings: The Water Authority, the Gas Board, British Telecom and the Electricity Board, all of whom have services in the bridgedeck. They adapted their pipes and cables to suit the new circumstances without making the usual charges, as their contribution to the project.

Shortly before the completion of Phase I, HRH The Duke of Edinburgh paid a formal visit to Telford New Town, on 14th July 1972. His tour of the New Town area included an inspection of the work so far completed, on the Iron Bridge. After answering his very erudite questions on what he saw, we went on to explain to him what we hoped to achieve in Phases II and III. It was indeed a happy occasion and I remember being most impressed by the evidence of the homework he must have done to prompt such knowledgeable questions and comments.

It was decided to invite tenders for Phase II, the placing of the invert slab. The successful tender was the Tarmac Construction Company supported by the Wolverhampton Piling Company. The sheet pile coffer dams would be a major part of the contract. Work on driving the piles started in the spring of 1973. By agreement with the River Authority work in the river was restricted to the summer months only, to avoid the aggravation of winter floods by the presence of coffer dams in the line of flow. Two steel and timber causeways were built across the river, one upstream and the other downstream of the coffer dams, to carry the pile driving rigs. Difficulties were encountered rightaway because the sheet piles refused to penetrate the mudstone bed rock. Only the use of the heaviest pile driving hammers available made any impression on the problem. But the mudstone had by no means capitulated as, after proving to be too hard to drive piles into in its undisturbed state, it degenerated into a porridge-like consistency when exposed to air and moisture by the excavation within the coffer dams. Fortunately further driving had been allowed for and water was kept out of the workings except for one spring when it found its way under the South abutment. The river was left to flow over the Northern half of its bed while the Southern half of the invert was being constructed. As each abutment had to be temporarily propped while the excavation of the bed and placing of the concrete took place, a small midstream section of invert was placed first and held in position by means of stressed anchorage cables down into the mudstone. This provided a firm basis for the temporary propping which consisted of massive steel girders.

Just when work was proceeding happily in the Southern half of the river bed the highest August flood in living memory occurred. Fortunately the River Authority had a most efficient early warning system, providing anticipated flood levels at given times and all material and equipment which might be washed away, as the coffer dams were overtopped, was removed to higher ground. Damage was kept to a minimum by the vigilance and foresight of the contractor and as soon as the inundation receded the coffer dams were pumped out and work continued unchecked. There was some public outcry in Ironbridge, that the bridge had been placed at risk by the presence of the coffer dams during the flood. In fact there was considerable erosion of the North bank, downstream of the bridge, resulting in extensive revetting with sheet piles backed with concrete and a length of masonry training wall had to be rebuilt.

It had always been a moot point as to whether it would prove possible to complete all the work in the river bed in one summer season. Now it was certain that there was no chance of this being achieved. Activity was therefore concentrated on completing the Southern half of the invert and leaving the river clear of obstruction for the winter, the coffer dams being removed as soon as they were no longer required.

During the winter of 1973-74 we assessed the situation at the North abutment so that plans could be made for a clear start as soon as we could get into the river, the following spring. These investigations resulted in a ledge being discovered, deep down the face of the abutment below the level of the clay of the river bed. The width of this ledge was about two feet at the downstream end of the abutment, running out to nothing at the upstream end. Presumably the wall had been started at an incorrect alignment and when the error had been spotted it had been decided not to dismantle the wall, so far built, but merely to start again at that level and to continue upwards on the correct alignment. It reminded us that the bridge had been built as a commercial proposition, for a quick return on the money invested. It was not the first evidence we had found of this but it did not, in our opinion, detract in any way from the work carried out in 1779. After all they could hardly have imagined anyone uncovering it a couple of hundred years later. In this instance it meant modifying the design of the invert and issuing fresh drawings resulting in extra work for the contractor, but at least the drawing office work was done in the winter and there was no delay to the work in the spring.

As soon as Tarmac were permitted to get into the river again, in April 1974 they did so to some effect and expedited the completion of the Northern half of the invert, in spite of the complication of the ledge. The structural element of the restoration was then complete. There remained the more superficial, but nevertheless important, tasks of relaying the roadway and footways, with further attention to the underground services, generally tidying up the masonry and the ironwork which had to be cleaned and repainted. The surrounding area had to be landscaped and this was done by Telford New Town Development Corporation.

It will be noticed, on site, that the concrete, which covers the front of the lower part of the abutments, is visible to some extent above normal water level. This was not due to lack of consideration. Many ways were suggested of concealing this concrete, which is essential to distribute the pressure over the face of the abutment and avoid overstressing the old masonry but all had eventually to be rejected.

At this stage the Department of the Environment took the bridge into guardianship. This meant not only that further work would be financed by the Treasury but that the Department would have complete control over what was to be done. Their first decision was that the road surface and all the filling material should be stripped from the deck of the bridge and all the underground services temporarily lifted while the deck was waterproofed. In the past the filling material, which consisted mainly of iron slag, had become saturated in wet weather, producing an acid solution which escaped through the joints in the deck and tended to corrode the ironwork beneath.

The Special Works Division was once again brought in to do this work. On completion of the waterproofing, using resin-bonded materials, and the relaying of the services, the filling material which had been removed was replaced by a special lightweight concrete which was laid to a smooth vertical alignment to carry the new surfacing. The somewhat inappropriate concrete kerbs at the edge of the footways were replaced by iron kerbs specially cast at the Coalbrookdale works. The raised footways and the kerbs are, in fact, an anachronism as the surface of the roadway stretched from parapet to parapet when the bridge was built. They do, however, serve the purpose of providing cover for the many pipes and cables which the bridge is obliged to carry and, for this reason the footways are preserved.

When the Severn Valley Railway was constructed, in the 1860s, the road level at the South end of the bridge was raised so as to cross the line on a level crossing. This resulted in the Toll House door step being well below the road. As the level crossing was no longer in use the road and footways were now restored to their original level. One of the conditions of the £50,000 contribution to the funds had been that the surfacing of the road and footways should not be coloured black, as is so often the case. A special macadam was therefore used which was bound by a colourless resin-based liquid instead of the usual black bitumen. Its durability had been proved by many years wear on some of London's busiest streets. The aggregate, in this case, was fine gravel of a rich golden colour, producing a very pleasing appearance though hardly a restoration of the original slag roadway.

While the County Special Works Division was engaged in these road works expert stonemasons of the Department of the Environment were attending to the stonework and replacing some of the more decayed parapet railings, at the South end of the bridge, with temporary brick parapets as a safety measure. Telford New Town Development Corporation now undertook a wide range of restoration work, starting with the landscaping of the environment of the bridge. The latter operation involved earthmoving which uncovered some partly demolished stone arches connected to the North abutment, though not strictly part of the bridge. These were duly restored and formed the basis for a viewing platform to enable visitors to enjoy the bridge in comfort.

The main item still outstanding was now the cleaning and painting of the ironwork. It had been established that in spite of the number of fractures there remained ample sound iron members to maintain the stability of the structure. Metallurgical tests had indicated that the 1779 cast-iron would not weld satisfactorily. So, though there had been suggestions about 'pointing up' the widest fractures with a resin-based plastic adhesive, it was now agreed to leave them alone. In any case, it was felt that some clearly visible cracks would serve as features of interest for the Museum Trust guides to point out to visitors.

In 1967 we had carried out extensive cleaning and painting trials, with the co-operation of Messrs. Griffiths, the Wolverhampton paint specialists, on selected areas of the ironwork. By this time, 1976, these trial areas had been subjected to nine years of weathering. Detailed records had been kept and were now forwarded to the Directorate, so that the full value of the trials could be made use of, as the Directorate would now be controlling the painting operation. In 1978 they carried out a trial of a system of cleaning by blasting with water containing some granular material, under high pressure. This trial was a spectacular success, from the cleaning point of view, but there were apparently problems connected with the pollution of the river by the lead in the old paint cleaned off.

The bridge was, however, still unpainted by the beginning of 1979, the bicentenary year of its construction. It is recorded that in 1879, when the bridge was one hundred years old, the occasion passed without any form of recognition. A number of interested parties, including the Museum Trust, Telford Development Corporation and the County Council were determined that such an omission would not occur again. A programme of almost a year of celebration was drawn up with due appointment of committees and so on. The earliest event, with the gorge still in the grip of winter, was the floodlighting of the cooling towers of the new Power Station. This was followed, in April when the essential darkness was still available at a resonable hour, by the formal switching on of the permanent floodlighting of the bridge itself.

About this time it became known that in July there would be a Royal Visit and the bridge would be inspected by the Prince of Wales. There was now no time to clean and paint the bridge before the event and it was quite obvious (especially under floodlighting) that it did need a lot of tidying up for such an occasion. Money was made available and it was agreed that the following works should be carried out if time permitted: the temporary brick parapets should be replaced by cast-iron railings; a length of old and decayed brick parapet should be replaced by matching stonework; the viewing platform should be brick paved, to match the Northern approach, with elegant brick steps connecting it to the bridge deck; the parapet railings on the bridge should be overhauled and painted and the whole thoroughly spruced up, short of the overall cleaning and painting.

A well-known local architect, Mr. David Lewis, chairman of the Action Committee, was engaged to prepare the necessary design drawings. Telford Development Corporation loaned their masonry restoration team under Mr. Bill Jenks and some specialists, particularly a welder experienced in working with certain types of cast-iron, were loaned by the County Council. A local firm undertook to fabricate the new railings and the Coalbrookdale foundry to cast a suitable plaque for Prince Charles to unveil. Work proceeded to considerable effect through the early part of the summer. The July celebrations were to consist of a Gala Day with bands and processions and general jollity, on the 2nd of the month, while anniversary day and the Royal Visit was on the 5th.

One of the final preparation activities by the County was to erect a temporary frame on which to mount the plaque to be unveiled. This was because with so many official bodies involved there was no hope of arriving at an agreement as to where it should be permanently attached to the bridge.

The Gala Day was a great success and a credit to the Museum Trust who had organized it. It is often an invideous task to try to mention some names on such an occasion but I would like to record the valiant work carried out by the late Mr. Fred Clamp, of the Trust, in this direction. Alas he is no longer with us, having spent his time lightening the burdens of all those with whom he came in contact.

On the morning of the 5th July a technician set out from the County Highway Depot with the plaque, which was inscribed "The Iron Bridge 1779-1979. This plaque to mark the bicentenary of the Iron Bridge was unveiled by H.R.H. The Prince of Wales on 5th July 1979". With the plaque were royal blue velvet curtains, complete with pelmet and draw cords. None of this could be left in position all night as they would almost certainly be pilfered as souvenirs. So here was a logistic problem, the solution of which depended very much on the resourcefulness of the technician. He had to convey this essential accessory to the occasion, which was bulky and pretty heavy, through the massed crowds to the bridge, set it up and see that it did not disappear before it was wanted. That he succeeded is greatly to his credit, But his problems were not over yet.

The weather was beautiful and a happy day was spent by all, including I hope,

The Plaque unveiled by H.R.H. The Prince of Wales in 1979.

His Royal Highness who had other functions to attend in addition to this one. When I was fortunate enough to be telling the Duke of Edinburgh, in 1972, what we hoped and intended to achieve, in the way of restoration, I little imagined that seven years later I would be pointing out to his eldest son what we had, in fact, done. I could not imagin a more enjoyable duty nor such a happy and satisfying occasion with which to end my life's career as Bridge Engineer a few days later.

A record of the events of that day would be incomplete without the rest of the saga of the technician with the plaque. As soon as the unveiling ceremony was complete and Prince Charles had been swept away in the royal car the crowd surged forward, surrounding the plaque on its temporary mounting. Among them was the technician who battled his way through somehow and started dismantling the plaque and its curtains. Immediately he was submerged in a mob of people, all determined to take away something as a souvenir. Struggling desperately he managed to foil the attempts of the crowd, to remove anything detachable, and complete his task. The only casualty was inflicted by a young lady who whipped a pair of scissors out of her handbag and snipped off the bobble from one of the draw cords and then, with her head well down, wormed her way through the crowds with all the speed and expertise of a rugby fly half. Eventually he managed to make his way with his heavy and vulnerable burden, back to the quiet side street where his van was parked. There he locked himself in until such time as the crowds had dispersed sufficiently for him to get away and return to the depot where the plaque remained for many months, until a situation had been agreed upon for its permanent fixture on the bridge.

The Iron Bridge was finally cleaned and painted, under the direction of the Department of the Environment, in 1980. The restoration could then be said to be complete.

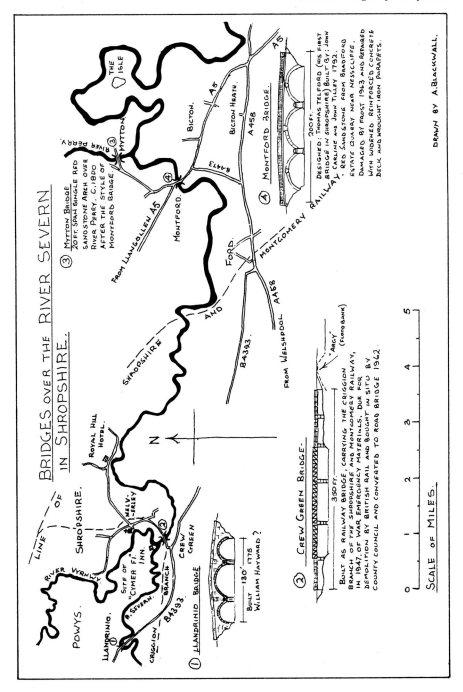

BRIDGES over the RIVER SEVERN
in SHROPSHIRE.

③ MYTTON BRIDGE
20 FT. SPAN SINGLE RFD
SANDSTONE ARCH OVER
RIVER PERRY, C.1800
AFTER THE STYLE OF
MONTFORD BRIDGE.

④ MONTFORD BRIDGE.

DESIGNED: THOMAS TELFORD (HIS FIRST
RAILWAY BRIDGE IN SHROPSHIRE) BUILT BY: JOHN
CARLINE AND JOHN TILLEY 1792.
RED SANDSTONE FROM BRADFORD
ESTATE QUARRY NEAR NESSCLIFFE.
DAMAGED BY FROST 1963 AND REPAIRED
WITH WIDENED REINFORCED CONCRETE
DECK AND WROUGHT IRON PARAPETS.

200 FT.

DRAWN BY A. BLACKWALL.

② CREW GREEN BRIDGE.

350 FT.

BUILT AS RAILWAY BRIDGE, CARRYING THE CRIGGION
BRANCH OF THE SHROPSHIRE AND MONTGOMERY RAILWAY,
IN 1847, OF WAR EMERGENCY MATERIALS. DUE FOR
DEMOLITION BY BRITISH RAIL AND BOUGHT IN SITU BY
COUNTY COUNCIL AND CONVERTED TO ROAD BRIDGE 1962.

① LLANDRINIO BRIDGE.

BUILT 1775
WILLIAM HAYWARD ?

130'

SCALE of MILES.

0   1   2   3   4   5

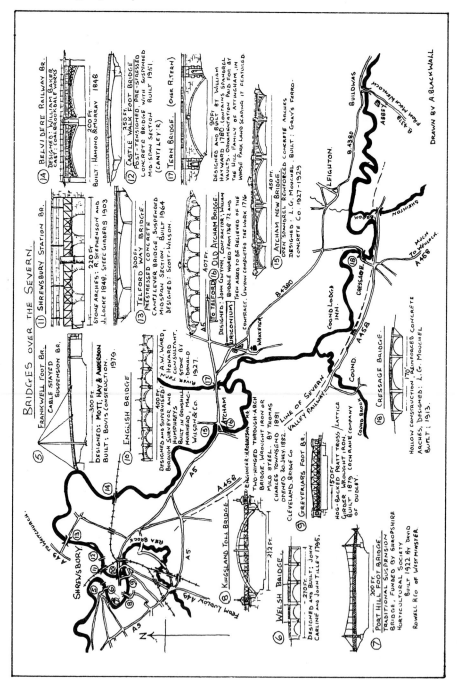

BRIDGES OVER THE SEVERN.

① SHREWSBURY STATION BR.

⑭ BELVIDERE RAILWAY BR.
DESIGNED: WILLIAM BAKER
CAST: COALBROOKDALE WORKS
BUILT: HAMONO & MURRAY 1848

⑫ CASTLE WALK FOOT BRIDGE
POST-TENSIONED PRE-STRESSED
CONCRETE BRIDGE WITH SUSPENDED
MID-SPAN SECTION. BUILT 1951
(CANTILEVER)

⑰ TERN BRIDGE. (OVER R.TERN)

④
220 FT. STONE ARCHES: R. STEPHENSON AND
J. LOCKE 1849. STEEL GIRDERS 1903

⑬ TELFORD WAY BRIDGE
300FT. PRESTRESSED CONCRETE
CANTILEVER BRIDGE SUSPENDED
MIDSPAN SECTION. BUILT 1964
DESIGNED: SCOTT-WILSON

⑯ OLD ATCHAM BRIDGE
DESIGNED: JOHN GWYNN, CONTRACTOR; WILLIAM
BUDDLE WORKED FROM 1768-72 AND
THEN ASKED TO BE RELIEVED OF THE
CONTRACT, GWYNN COMPLETED THE WORK 1776

To TELFORD

URICONIUM

WROXETER

DESIGNED AND BUILT BY WILLIAM
HAYWARD 1780. (CONTAINS SPANDREL
VAULTS. FOUNDATION PADS FOR BY
THE HILL FAMILY OF ATTINGHAM, IN
WHOSE PARK LAND SCALING IT FEATURED.

⑮ ATCHAM NEW BRIDGE
OPEN SPANDREL REINFORCED CONCRETE ARCHES.
DESIGNED: L. G. MOUCHEL. BUILT: GRAY'S FERRO-
CONCRETE CO. 1927-1929
450 FT.

⑤ FRANKWELL FOOT BR.
300 FT. CABLE STAYED
SUSPENSION BR.
DESIGNED: MOTT, HAY & ANDERSON
BUILT: BOVIS CONSTRUCTION.
1979.

⑩ ENGLISH BRIDGE
400 FT.
DESIGNED AND SUPERVISED: J. A. W. WARD,
BOROUGH SURVEYOR AND J. HOWARD
HUMPHREYS L CONSULTANT.
BUILT IN GRINSHILL STONE BY
MOORHEAD, MAC-DONALD
WILSON & CO. 1927.

ATCHAM

A5

SEVERN VALLEY RAILWAY

LINE OF SEVERN

COUND BROOK

COUND

COUND LODGE INN

LEIGHTON.
B.4380

BUILDWAS

ABBEY

FROM MUCH WENLOCK
B.4378

To MUCH WENLOCK
A.4169

CRESSAGE
A.458

B.4380

SHEINTON.

BANDON

DRAWN BY A. BLACKWALL

⑱ CRESSAGE BRIDGE.
170 FT.
HOLLOW CONSTRUCTION. REINFORCED CONCRETE
ARCHES, DESIGNED: L. G. MOUCHEL.
BUILT; 1913.

⑭

⑪ ENGINEER : WROUGHT IRON
TWO-HINGED THROUGH-ARCH
BRIDGE, WROUGHT IRON OR
MILD STEEL BY THOMAS
CHARLES TOWNSEND
OPENED 20 JULY 1882.
CLEVELAND BRIDGE CO

⑨ GREYFRIARS FOOT BR.
150 FT.
HOG-BACKED PRATT TRUSS/LATTICE
GIRDER WROUGHT IRON.
BUILT 1875 COCHRANE COMPANY
OF DUDLEY.

A5

SHREWSBURY

REA BROOK

A.49 To WHITCHURCH

⑬

A.458

⑧ KINGSLAND TOLL BRIDGE.
212 FT.

WELSH BRIDGE.
220 FT.
DESIGNED AND BUILT: JOHN
CARLINE AND JOHN TILLEY 1795.

⑥

FROM LUDLOW A49

⑦ PORT HILL FOOT BRIDGE
200 FT.
TRADITIONAL SUSPENSION
BRIDGE. FUNDED BY SHROPSHIRE
HORTICULTURAL SOCIETY
BUILT 1922 BY DAVID
ROWELL R.'D OF WESTMINSTER.

A5

N

114

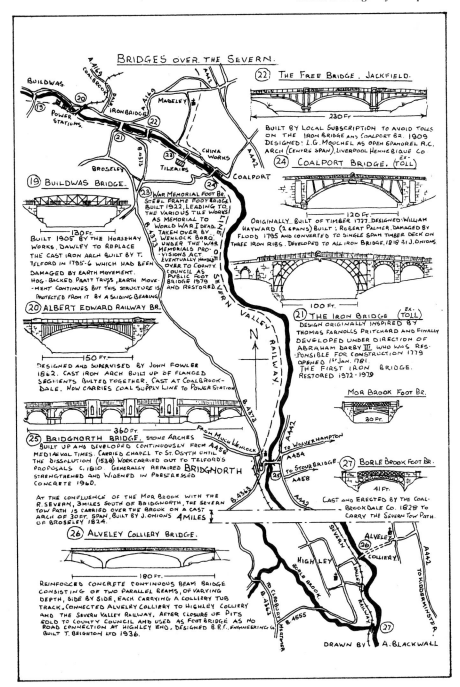

BRIDGES OVER THE SEVERN.

BUILDWAS

POWER STATIONS

IRONBRIDGE

MADELEY

BROSELEY

CHINA WORKS

TILERIES

COALPORT

⑲ BUILDWAS BRIDGE.

—130 FT.—
BUILT 1905 BY THE HORSEHAY WORKS, DAWLEY TO REPLACE THE CAST IRON ARCH BUILT BY T. TELFORD IN 1795-6 WHICH HAD BEEN DAMAGED BY EARTH MOVEMENT. HOG-BACKED PRATT TRUSS, EARTH MOVEMENT CONTINUES BUT THIS STRUCTURE IS PROTECTED FROM IT BY A SLIDING BEARING.

⑳ ALBERT EDWARD RAILWAY BR.

—150 FT.—
DESIGNED AND SUPERVISED BY JOHN FOWLER 1862. CAST IRON ARCH BUILT UP OF FLANGED SEGMENTS BOLTED TOGETHER. CAST AT COALBROOK-DALE. NOW CARRIES COAL SUPPLY LINE TO POWER STATION.

—360 FT.—
㉕ BRIDGNORTH BRIDGE. STONE ARCHES
BUILT UP AND DEVELOPED CONTINUOUSLY FROM MEDIAEVAL TIMES. CARRIED CHAPEL TO ST. OSYTH UNTIL THE DISSOLUTION (1538) WORK CARRIED OUT TO TELFORD'S PROPOSALS c.1810. GENERALLY REPAIRED, STRENGTHENED AND WIDENED IN PRESTRESSED CONCRETE 1960.

AT THE CONFLUENCE OF THE MOR BROOK WITH THE R. SEVERN, 3 MILES SOUTH OF BRIDGNORTH, THE SEVERN TOW PATH IS CARRIED OVER THE BROOK ON A CAST ARCH OF 30 FT. SPAN, BUILT BY J. ONIONS 4 MILES OF BROSELEY 1824.

㉖ ALVELEY COLLIERY BRIDGE.

—180 FT.—
REINFORCED CONCRETE CONTINUOUS BEAM BRIDGE CONSISTING OF TWO PARALLEL BEAMS, OF VARYING DEPTH, SIDE BY SIDE, EACH CARRYING A COLLIERY TUB TRACK. CONNECTED ALVELEY COLLIERY TO HIGHLEY COLLIERY AND THE SEVERN VALLEY RAILWAY. AFTER CLOSURE OF PITS SOLD TO COUNTY COUNCIL AND USED AS FOOT BRIDGE AS NO ROAD CONNECTION AT HIGHLEY END. DESIGNED B.R.C. ENGINEERING Co. BUILT T. BEIGHTON LTD 1936.

㉒ THE FREE BRIDGE, JACKFIELD.

—230 FT.—
BUILT BY LOCAL SUBSCRIPTION TO AVOID TOLLS ON THE IRON BRIDGE AND COALPORT BR. 1909 DESIGNED: L.G. MOUCHEL AS OPEN SPANDREL R.C. ARCH (CENTRE SPAN). LIVERPOOL HENNEBIQUE Co.

㉔ COALPORT BRIDGE. (TOLL) (EX-)

—120 FT.—
ORIGINALLY BUILT OF TIMBER 1777. DESIGNED: WILLIAM HAYWARD (2 SPANS) BUILT: ROBERT PALMER. DAMAGED BY FLOOD 1795 AND CONVERTED TO SINGLE SPAN TIMBER DECK ON THREE IRON RIBS. DEVELOPED TO ALL IRON BRIDGE, 1818 BY J. ONIONS.

㉓ WAR MEMORIAL FOOT BR.
STEEL FRAME FOOTBRIDGE BUILT 1922. LEADING TO THE VARIOUS TILE WORKS AS MEMORIAL TO WORLD WAR I DEAD. TAKEN OVER BY WENLOCK BORO' UNDER THE WAR MEMORIALS PROVISIONS ACT EVENTUALLY HANDED OVER TO COUNTY COUNCIL AS PUBLIC FOOT BRIDGE 1979 AND RESTORED.

—100 FT.—
㉑ THE IRON BRIDGE (TOLL) (EX-)
DESIGN ORIGINALLY INSPIRED BY THOMAS FARNOLLS PRITCHARD AND FINALLY DEVELOPED UNDER DIRECTION OF ABRAHAM DARBY III WHO WAS RESPONSIBLE FOR CONSTRUCTION 1779 OPENED 1st JAN. 1781. THE FIRST IRON BRIDGE. RESTORED 1972-1979

MOR BROOK FOOT BR.

—30 FT.—

㉗ BORLE BROOK FOOT BR.

—41 FT.—
CAST AND ERECTED BY THE COALBROOK DALE Co. 1828 TO CARRY THE SEVERN TOW PATH.

SEVERN VALLEY RAILWAY.

N

FROM MUCH WENLOCK
TO WOLVERHAMPTON
TO STOURBRIDGE

BRIDGNORTH

TO KIDDERMINSTER.

ALVELEY
COLLIERY

HIGHLEY

BORLE BROOK

SEVERN VALLEY RAILWAY

DRAWN BY A. BLACKWALL

Pictorial Glossary

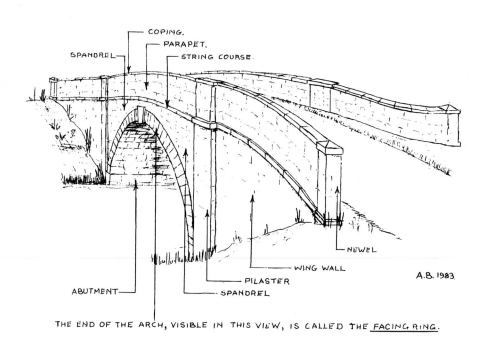

THE END OF THE ARCH, VISIBLE IN THIS VIEW, IS CALLED THE FACING RING.

Pictorial Glossary (cont.)

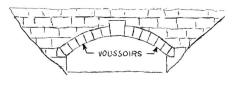

SEGMENTAL ARCH.

PLAIN VOUSSOIRS IN THE FACING RING.

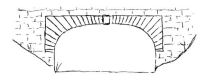

ELLIPTICAL ARCH.

ORNAMENTAL VOUSSOIRS IN THE FACING RING.

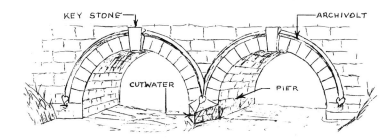

SEMI-CIRCULAR ARCHES WITH MOULDED ARCHIVOLTS AND PROMINENT KEYSTONES.

EXTRADOS

INTRADOS

CARTOUCHE.

SEGMENTAL ARCH

WITH STEPPED EXTRADOS

A.B. 1983

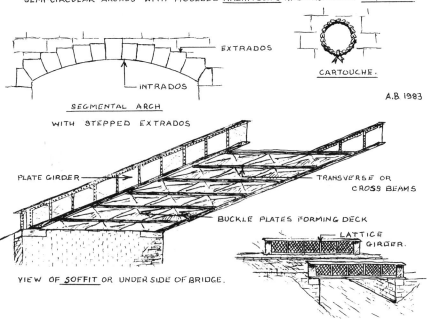

PLATE GIRDER

TRANSVERSE OR CROSS BEAMS

BUCKLE PLATES FORMING DECK

LATTICE GIRDER.

VIEW OF SOFFIT OR UNDER SIDE OF BRIDGE.

TWO THROUGH-GIRDER BRIDGES.

117

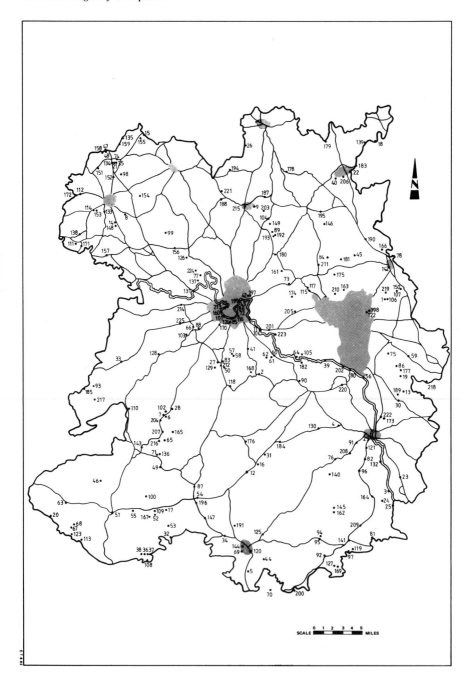

The Bridges

Bridge	No.	Map Ref.
Abbey Farm C B	*1*	SJ735140
Acton Burnell Hall	*2*	SJ536024
Alveley	*3*	SO748839
Ash	*4*	SO667943
Ashford	*5*	SO520711
Ashgrove No. 1	*6*	SO381952
Ashgrove No. 2	*7*	SO382952
Aston Hall	*8*	SJ320273
Aston Wem	*9*	SJ530287
Atcham	*10*	SJ540093
Atcham New	*11*	SJ540092
Bache Mill	*12*	SO504856
Badger	*13*	SO771995
Ball	*14*	SJ304266
Bartons	*15*	SJ354403
Beambridge (Corve)	*16*	SO533882
Beambridge Aston	*17*	SO388813
Bearstone	*18*	SJ725389
Beckbury	*19*	SJ758015
Beguildy	*20*	SO192803
Belmont C B	*21*	SJ305357
Berrisford	*22*	SJ684343
Blunder	*23*	SO767855
Borle Mill	*24*	SO733826
Borle Brook F B	*25*	SO753817
Brickwalls C B	*26*	SJ512378
Bridge Farm	*27*	SJ468044
Bridges	*28*	SO398963
Bridgnorth	*29*	SO718930
Broad	*30*	SO762982
Broadstone	*31*	SO543897
Broadward	*32*	SO395767
Brockton	*33*	SJ318044
Bromfield	*34*	SO482770
Brook House	*35*	SJ305358
Bucknell Church	*36*	SO354740
Bucknell East	*37*	SO358739
Bucknell West	*38*	SO351740
Buildwas	*39*	SJ645045
Buntingsdale Hall	*40*	SJ658331
Cantlop	*41*	SJ517063
Cascade Arch	*42*	SJ524147
Castle Walk F B	*43*	SJ499130
Caynham	*44*	SO543729
Caynton Mill	*45*	SJ693214
Cefn Einion	*46*	SO285862
Chirk	*47*	SJ290373
Chirk Bank C B	*48*	SJ371292
Choulton	*49*	SO380877
Church	*50*	SJ482034
Clun	*51*	SO300808
Clunbury	*52*	SO371807
Clungunford	*53*	SO395786
Clunsford	*54*	SO437828
Clunton F B	*55*	SO337813
Coalport	*56*	SJ702021
Condover Hall	*57*	SJ493058
Condover New	*58*	SJ497055
Cosford	*59*	SJ781046
Cound	*60*	SJ558057
Cound Arbor	*61*	SJ555053
Cound Stank	*62*	SJ545053
Cow Hall	*63*	SO224820
Cressage	*64*	SJ594045
Criftin	*65*	SO385917
Cruckton	*66*	SJ433098
Cwm Brain	*67*	SO232779
Cwm Collo	*68*	SO237784
Dinham	*69*	SO507745
Easton Court C B	*70*	SO556682
Eaton	*71*	SO375897
English	*72*	SJ497124
Ercall Mill	*73*	SJ585163
Esgob Mill	*74*	SJ309362
Evelith Mill	*75*	SJ743051
Faintree Tunnel	*76*	SO657889
Fitz	*77*	SJ444180
Forton	*78*	SJ750208
Frankwell	*79*	SJ490128
Free	*80*	SJ681033
Furnace Mill	*81*	SO721766
Glazeley	*82*	SO704885
Gonsal	*83*	SJ477043
Great Bolas	*84*	SJ648208
Greyfriars F B	*85*	SJ496121
Grindle Forge	*86*	SJ753034
Grove (Strefford)	*87*	SO433847
Hanwood	*88*	SJ440095
Harcourt Mill	*89*	SJ560247
Harley	*90*	SJ600011
Harpswood	*91*	SO692916
Hay	*92*	SO642737
Hockleton	*93*	SJ275003
Hopton Court	*94*	SO639769
Hopton Wafers	*95*	SO637765
Horseford	*96*	SO699865
Houghtons Pole	*97*	SO682742
Iron Mills	*98*	SJ318334
Jubilee	*99*	SJ397244
Kempton	*100*	SO357827
Kingsland Toll	*101*	SJ488121
Kinnerton	*102*	SO394928
Lea	*103*	SJ419083
Lee	*104*	SJ549268
Leighton	*105*	SJ610056
Lilleshall Abbey C B	*106*	SJ736140
Lilleshall Drive C B	*107*	SJ752160
Lingen	*108*	SO358729
Little Brampton	*109*	SO371811
Little Tasker	*110*	SO325961
Llanyblodwel	*111*	SJ242228
Llawnt	*112*	SJ249308
Lloyney	*113*	SO245761
Llwynymaen	*114*	SJ270283
Long Mill	*115*	SJ620154
Longden Coleham	*116*	SJ498123
Longdon-on-Tern	*117*	SJ616155
Longnor	*118*	SJ487007
Lower Forge F B	*119*	SO688748
Ludford	*120*	SO512743
Marlbrook	*121*	SO708905
Mary Anne Perry's CB	*122*	SJ705125
Melinagrogue	*123*	SO232770
Meole Brace	*124*	SJ490107
Middleton	*125*	SO540770
Milford	*126*	SJ421211
Millbrook	*127*	SO656724
Minsterley	*128*	SJ374051
Moat Cottages	*129*	SJ452033
Monkhopton	*130*	SO627936
Montford	*131*	SJ432153
Morbrook F B	*132*	SO733887
Morda	*133*	SJ288282
Morton Hall	*134*	SJ300356
Mouses	*135*	SJ392315
Myndtown	*136*	SO379898
Mytton	*137*	SJ440170
Nant Mawr	*138*	SJ249244
Napeley Lodge	*139*	SJ707384
Neenton Dairy	*140*	SO646872
New	*141*	SO680763
Newport C B	*142*	SJ743194
Newton	*143*	SO346909
Old Corve	*144*	SO511753
Old Roman	*145*	SO663815
Ollerton	*146*	SJ645261
Onibury	*147*	SO454790
Paint Mill	*148*	SJ304258
Paper Mill	*149*	SJ558258
Pave Lane C B	*150*	SJ757163
Pen-y-Bont	*151*	SJ277345
Pentre Wern	*152*	SJ302328
Pen-y-Llan Lane	*153*	SJ276282
Perry Farm	*154*	SJ347302
Plas Thomas	*155*	SJ352392
Platt Mill	*156*	SJ403222
Pont Fadoc	*157*	SJ211293
Pont Faen	*158*	SJ280371
Pont-y-Blew	*159*	SJ310382
Porthill F B	*160*	SJ485126
Poynton	*161*	SJ570188
Prescott Mill	*162*	SO662810
Preston C B	*163*	SJ680156
Priors Moor	*164*	SO715834
Prolley Moor	*165*	SO394928
Pulestone	*166*	SJ734219
Purslow Clun	*167*	SO361805
Radnal	*168*	SJ525026
Rea, Neen Sollars	*169*	SO664724
Red Hill Colliery	*170*	SJ469096
Rhyd Meredyth	*171*	SJ252225
Rhydycroesau	*172*	SJ242308
Rindleford F B	*173*	SO738956
Rodington	*174*	SJ590143
Rodway	*175*	SJ663182
Rushbury Pack Horse	*176*	SO513916
Ryton	*177*	SJ759026
Sandford	*178*	SJ581341
Shavington	*179*	SJ644389
Shawbury	*180*	SJ562213
Sheep	*181*	SJ671208
Sheinton	*182*	SJ608040
Shiffords	*183*	SJ691348
Shipton	*184*	SO568917
Shiregrove	*185*	SO249996
Shrewsbury Station	*186*	SJ495128
Soulton	*187*	SJ546303
Spendford	*188*	SJ479298
Stableford	*189*	SO760988
Standford	*190*	SJ704237
Stanton Lacy	*191*	SO495788
Stanton Mill	*192*	SJ567241
Stanton River	*193*	SJ565239
Starks C B	*194*	SJ492346
Stoke River	*195*	SJ637278
Stokesay	*196*	SO438819
Sundorne	*197*	SJ524147
Teagues C B	*198*	SJ708127
Telford Way	*199*	SJ506141
Tenbury	*200*	SJ596686
Tern	*201*	SJ553093
The Iron Bridge	*202*	SJ672033
Thistleford	*203*	SJ543281
Upper Mill	*204*	SO379945
Walcot Mill	*205*	SJ594124
Walkmill (M. Drayton)	*206*	SJ672336
Walkmill Wentnor	*207*	SO379928
Walls Batch	*208*	SO678899
Walltown	*209*	SO697786
Wappenshall Junction C B	*210*	SJ663146
Waters Upton	*211*	SJ631194
Wayford	*212*	SJ475038
Welsh	*213*	SJ489128
Welshmans Ford	*214*	SJ414132
Wem	*215*	SJ512286
Whitcot	*216*	SO378917
Whittrey	*217*	SO272982
Wildecote	*218*	SJ806010
Wildmoor Lane C B	*219*	SJ736158
Willey Park Boreton	*220*	SJ669006
Wolverley	*221*	SJ474313
Woodbridge	*56*	SJ702021
Worfe	*222*	SO733958
Wroxeter	*223*	SJ564081
Yeaton	*224*	SJ434193
Yockleton	*225*	SJ396100

Bibliography

Most of the historical references and all the quoted passages, in this book, are from a collection of documents in the possession of the County Archivist and usually referred to as the *Deposited Bridge Plans.* The collection was assembled and catalogued in 1902.

Further historical information has been noted from the following publications:-

The Ancient Bridges of Wales and Western England. E. Jervoise. Pub. E. P. Publishing Ltd., 1976 (originally 1936).

The Book of Bridges. Martin Hayden. Pub. Marshall Cavendish, 1976.

Transactions of the Shropshire Archaeological and Natural History Society, Volumes XLII and XLIX.

A Span of Bridges. H. J. Hopkins. Pub. David and Charles, 1970.

British Bridges. Pub. Public Works, Roads and Transport Congress, 1933.

The Iron Bridge at Coalbrookdale. Robert Maguire and Peter Matthews. *Architectural Association Journal,* July - August 1958.

The New Ferro-concrete Bridge at Ironbridge, Coalbrookdale. Benjamin Brear. *Ferro-concrete Magazine,* No. 1, Vol. 1, July 1909.

Coalport Bridge; a study in Historical Interpretation. Barrie Trinder. *Industrial Archaeology Review,* Vol III, No. 2, Spring 1979.

Shropshire and its Rulers. G. C. Baugh and D. C. Cox. Shropshire Libraries 1979.

Thomas Telford. L. T. C. Rolt. Pub. Longmans, Green and Co. 1958.

Royal Escape. Georgette Heyer. Pub. William Heinemann, 1938.

The English Bridge, Shrewsbury. Official Programme (of opening ceremony which did not take place) and Souvenir. Pub. Wilding and Son 1927.

The Iron Bridge. Neil Cossons and Barrie Trinder. Pub. Ironbridge Gorge Museum Trust and Moonraker Press, 1979.

Alveley Bridge. A. P. Mason. *Concrete and Constructional Engineering,* August 1937.

Index

Illustrations indicated by page numbers in **bold** type.